HIDDEN TREASURES

BEDFORDSHIRE

Edited by Simon Harwin

First published in Great Britain in 2002 by
YOUNG WRITERS
Remus House,
Coltsfoot Drive,
Peterborough, PE2 9JX
Telephone (01733) 890066

HB ISBN 0 75433 896 7
SB ISBN 0 75433 897 5

FOREWORD

This year, the Young Writers' Hidden Treasures competition proudly presents a showcase of the best poetic talent from over 72,000 up-and-coming writers nationwide.

Young Writers was established in 1991 and we are still successful, even in today's technologically-led world, in promoting and encouraging the reading and writing of poetry.

The thought, effort, imagination and hard work put into each poem impressed us all, and once again, the task of selecting poems was a difficult one, but nevertheless, an enjoyable experience.

We hope you are as pleased as we are with the final selection and that you and your family continue to be entertained with *Hidden Treasures Bedfordshire* for many years to come.

CONTENTS

Overstone Combined School

Jonathan Hill	88
Ben Latimer	89
Sam West	89
Abigail Fairbairn	90
Harriet Gordon-Head	91
Leah Fitzgerald	92
Jessica Axten	93
Danny Wright	94
David Jarman	94
Edward Pugh	95
Alexandra Gordon-Stuart	96
Edward Fairbairn	96
Freya Hawkins	97
Jessica Smith	98
Daniel Rixson	98
Samantha Foot	99
Harry Tregartha	99
Amy Goss	100
Ruby Lewis	100
Chloe Malin	101
Kieran Bunce	101
Jake Stanmore	102
Jenni Duncumb	103

Pirton Hill Junior School

Nathan James	104
Usman Shazad	104
Antonio Brownie	105
Sophie Neate	105
Charis Blake	106
Jack Penman	106
Aisling Maynard	107
Richenda Leigh Heyes	107
Daniel Hill	108
Katie Fairall	108
Conor Clarke	109
Danielle Benson	110

The Poems

HIDDEN TREASURES

A hidden treasure is not just a treasure
Chest at the bottom of the ocean.

> It is
> A person,
> Not just a person,
> Someone who loves you,
> Cares about you,
> They will help you if you get hurt.
>
> If you are nice to someone,
> You are a treasure to them.
> They will love you,
> Care about you,
> Help you if you get hurt.

These are the real hidden treasures.

Adam Grimes (10)
Alban CE Middle School

HIDDEN TREASURE

Hidden treasures under the sea
Where will you find it and what will it be?
Will there be gold
And will it be old?
Maybe silver rings
Or even money.
It is precious to me
So I keep swimming in the sea.
No one will find it,
I hope,
But only me.

Mark Harlow (11)
Alban CE Middle School

HIDDEN TREASURES

H idden
I n the sea
D istant
D ominions
E verywhere
N ear and far.

T reasure
R ubies
E specially gold
A nd it is heavy
S uper riches
U nusual plants
R ich value
E verywhere
S uperb goods.

Mark Shreeves (11)
Alban CE Middle School

MY HIDDEN TREASURES

T orch for lighting the way,
R ocket fireworks for fun,
E verlasting gumballs, lots of chewing,
A BB gun for defence,
S wiss pocket knife is useful too,
U ltimate loud caps to keep the neighbours away,
R ecording pen for mischief,
E ggs, rotten of course,
S tink bombs for a quick getaway.

Josh Brown (10)
Alban CE Middle School

FINDING HIDDEN TREASURE

H idden in the darkest depths,
I n chests bound like prisoners of war,
D eeper,
D arker,
E verywhere around is full of stillness,
N ot a sound to be heard.

T reasure is somewhere here,
R ound the corner hidden like a child playing hide and seek,
E choing voices in the strange caves,
A round the walls like a bouncing ball,
S omething's here,
U nder the rock
R eaching under,
E verywhere is full of excitement like a child's party
        Because the treasure is found.

Rebekah Crossley (10)
Alban CE Middle School

WHAT ARE . . . THE STARS?

The stars are burning tennis balls
Fired from a giant's tennis racquet.

Fireflies flying on the shadowy pavement
When they get tired they just disappear.

The stars are glitter
Glued on a sheet of dark blue paper.

That's what stars are.

Fraser Everest (11)
Alban CE Middle School

MERMAIDS' LAGOON

There is a sea so still and clear,
you could just shed a mystical tear,
Its beauty cannot be seen above,
But down below there's much more love.

The calm seas hit the rocks,
And the tall grey boats leave the docks,
Deep in the clear blue seas,
Where dolphins jump upon the breeze.

Mermaids splash and swim around,
You can't wait to hear the misty sound,
They glide through the waters with their fishy tails,
Alongside the ships, dolphins and whales.

Their hair so beautiful, blonde and brown,
So beautiful it would look with a crown,
And as they glide through the oceans deep,
There is a secret they must keep.

Beauty, beauty everywhere,
With gold and brown, wispy hair,
How I wish that they could stay
But instead they just secretly glide away.

Emma Robertson (9)
Alban CE Middle School

HIDDEN TREASURES

Hidden treasures beneath the sea,
precious to me.
The treasure is hidden
I don't want anyone to have it,
It's mine, it's golden but covered in a little dirt.
That can be sorted
No one knows where it is.

I covered it in sand and seaweed,
No one can find it,
I put the treasure there,
It's my greatest possession.
I'm only a little mermaid
With very few treasures.

Leanne Kenna (10)
Alban CE Middle School

TREASURE HUNT

I'm going on a treasure hunt to see what I can find,
I'm going on a treasure hunt and what I find is mine,
Gold or silver I don't mind.
I'm going on a treasure hunt to see what I can find.

I'm going on a treasure hunt, I look through the park,
I can't find anything, I think it's because it's dark,
But just as I was going I found a yellow spark,
I'm going on a treasure hunt, I look through the park.

I'm going on a treasure hunt, it's not silver or gold,
I think it's just a penny, very, very old,
I didn't say no, and I didn't say bum!
I just thanked the Lord I had my mum.

I'm going on a treasure hunt, I look through my home,
'There was nothing in the park,' I said. I didn't moan,
I just sat at the table looking very small,
But I said to my family,
'You're the best treasure of all!'

Jodie Knott (10)
Alban CE Middle School

HIDDEN TREASURES

On Saturday, Mum said I couldn't play;
I thought it would be a really bad day,
She said I had to clean my room;
My head was filled with doom and gloom.
But I had yet to find hidden treasures.

I delved to the depths of my floor;
No longer could I see the door.
Toys and books everywhere;
Things I'd thrown down without a care.
But underneath there were hidden treasures.

I found a book I'd never read
At the foot of the unmade bed;
Two Airfix kits left undone;
A first prize medal I had won.
All were hidden treasures.

It's amazing what you can find;
It might seem like a terrible grind,
Spending just a little time;
But it may not be such a crime,
When you find hidden treasures.

Alistair McDougall (11)
Alban CE Middle School

WHAT IS . . . THE HAIL?

A translucent football down from Heaven,
A white light bulb falling from the sky,
A shiny, white bowling ball that God dropped down to Earth,
Heavy bubbles from God's basin,
That's what hail is.

Joshua Palmer (11)
Alban CE Middle School

HIDDEN TREASURES

Pebbles, beaches or under the sea,
Treasures to find for you and me,
I've got them and found them,
But in the end,
What treasure is better than a brilliant friend?

Pirate ships or castaways,
Will search for months or weeks or days,
I've got them and found them,
But in the end
What treasure is better than a brilliant friend?

No crosses, no flag poles, no pirate ship's crew,
Just a wonderful person awaiting you,
I've got them and found them,
But in the end,
Nothing comes close to my best friend.

Lisa Withey (11)
Alban CE Middle School

HIDDEN TREASURE

I dived down under the sea,
So well hidden it was hard to see,
I reached the dark brown box,
'What is in it?' I asked myself.
I opened it with difficulty,
It was covered in seaweed,
Oh my gosh!
Lots of money and jewellery,
All so precious, all so delicate,
This can be my secret.

Kerry-Ann Hart (10)
Alban CE Middle School

JONATHAN KOO

There once was a boy called Jonathan Koo
who went to sea in the Peggy Sue,
One night as they were drifting along
Jonathan heard a very queer song.
He went outside to look around
and while he was looking at the ground,
There was then an awful gale
as if a dragon was swishing its tail.
Jonathan fell off the boat into the sea
and said to himself 'This is my land.'
Just then there were some terrible thumps and a roar
as if someone was knocking down the door.
A dragon came running tall and strong,
he was quite fat and also long.
Jonathan shouted, 'Help me, please,'
and then heard something wheeze.
'Jonathan, dive into the sea,
he cannot swim, he's like a bee,
but you can swim so very far,
soaring soundly like a star!'
After that Jonathan swam like a fish,
but then one day he found a gold dish,
under the dish there was a box
and in the box there was . . . *treasure.*

Natalie Fraser (10)
Alban CE Middle School

WEATHER TREASURE

The sky is as black as thunder,
The mist is like thick paint,
The clouds are like snowballs,
The sea is as rough as a stone,
Bubbling away like the lava from a volcano.
The wind blew the sand against my leg
As if it was burning fire,
The distant rocks were jagged
And looked like piercing needles
However they were as smooth as lino,
They were wet to the touch,
The rocks were covered with seaweed
Be careful treading.
Ahoy! What's this nestled amongst the seaweed?
A box or a chest I can't decide
It is like an evergreen
It is as cold as ice
It is like an overgrown hill,
My footsteps are as quiet as mice,
Oh! Now what's inside!
A ray of sunshine, I decide
I had opened the chest of weather treasure,
It used to be as cold as ice,
And now it is really nice.

Carly McGrath (9)
Alban CE Middle School

SECRETS OF THE SEA

I've heard it said that long ago
beyond the sands in the sea below,
along the floor of the deepest depth,
a chest of gold and jewels are kept.
A gathering of stolen booty
a secret stash of highest beauty.
A towering pile of glittering treasure,
a heap of rich everlasting pleasure.
But far from here the treasure is hidden
and all but sea life is forbidden.
For these beautiful jewels belong to the sea,
and may never be seen by you or me.
The secrets of the sea may one day be told,
and the dark mystery of her treasure may one day unfold.

Lucy Eaton (9)
Alban CE Middle School

THE SEA

Listen to the sea . . .

She floats up as clouds
She falls down as rain
She soaks through the earth
Then she comes back again.

Listen to the sea . . .

She slips over the pebbles
She creeps in streams
She runs down to rivers
And peeps through your dreams.

Sameera Raja (10)
Denbigh Junior School

THE BAT OF BATS

I am the bat of bats
I am the vampire bat
I have long, sharp teeth
And two demon eyes
I am the vampire bat.
I hunt at night for human
Blood
I am the vampire bat.
I spread my demon wings
And grab my victim
Then I put my sharp
Scary fangs into their
Neck.
I am the only vampire bat.

I am the bat of bats!

Nurhan Miah (8)
Denbigh Junior School

CLOUDS

The clouds are moving around the sky
They make white T-shirts on the washing line look dull and grey
The clouds go around, meeting each other and making friends
As the clouds get bored, they chat with one another
When they are bored with chatting they start to argue
And then they start fighting
As they argue they get darker and darker until . . .

Bang! Crash!

And one of them is hurt and upset
And their tears wet the whole world.

Sumaira Hussain (10)
Denbigh Junior School

DINNER

'Yuck!'
I heard someone say it.
Slurp!
Oh no! My nephew did it.
Munch!
Someone is eating crisps.
Clang!
Oops! That was my spoon
Hic, hic!
That was my sister.
Fizzzz!
That was the drink
Burp!
Was that me?

Syeda Ferdush (10)
Denbigh Junior School

THE WEATHER

Bang!
The thunder comes out of the sky
Drip!
The rain bounces off the rooftop
Squeak!
Goes the rat behind the gas cooker.
Whoosh!
The wind blows down the street.
Woof!
Goes the dog in our garden.
Buzz!
The flashlight outside is fused.

Sufian Mumtaz (9)
Denbigh Junior School

MY BIG SISTER

Who's the one who shouts at me?
Who makes me climb up a tree?
My big sister.

Who's the one who annoys me lots?
Who makes me wash all the pots?
My big sister.

Who's the person who comes from school?
Who's the one who thinks she's cool?
My big sister.

Who's the person who broke my game?
Who's the one who gave me the blame?
My big sister!

Kulsuma Begum (8)
Denbigh Junior School

LOVE AND HATE

Love is red
It smells like fresh roses
It tastes like ice cream
It sounds like romantic music
It feels like soft fur
It can live in everyone's heart.

Hate is black
It smells like burnt fish
It tastes like hot chilli
It sounds like drums banging
It feels like a crocodile's teeth
It lives in a cold, dark cave.

Rajia Begum (10)
Denbigh Junior School

CHRISTMAS

C olourful lights that twinkle and shine
H appy children laughing and playing
R obins singing a Christmas song
I cing on a Christmas cake
S anta Claus comes down the chimney
T winkling star on the Christmas tree
M ary had a special baby
A ngels celebrated his birth
S parkling lights, flashing in the darkness.

Shaila Mahmood (8)
Denbigh Junior School

NEW YEAR

N avy blue fireworks light up the sky
E veryone turns to their neighbours to say
'W e wish you a happy New Year.'

Y ears change so fast
E ach of us saying goodbye to the old.
A s at midnight it leaves
R eady for the birth of a brand new year.

Saara Najjar (8)
Denbigh Junior School

THE BEACH

Stretched out sleepily in the shade
On a day when the sun is as fierce as a bright red laser
I'm feeling very hot and sticky
And my face is like a red ball of lava.

The sea looks like a bright blue paper, with shaving foam on top
As I head towards it for a swim,
But the sand tickles my feet, like there are ants everywhere
Making me run as though I've got a cactus in my pants.

Thanbirul Haque (10)
Denbigh Junior School

CHRISTMAS

C   hristmas is celebrated every year
H   appy people being kind to each other
R   obins are singing. Can you hear?
I   cing on the cake makes it lovely to eat
S   o many people are excited about Christmas
T   he people are happy when they meet
M   any decorations are put up on the walls
A   ll of the people are excited
S   chool children make decorations for the hall.

Stephanie Rajroop (8)
Denbigh Junior School

NEW YEAR

N   ew Year is here
E   veryone will enjoy themselves
W   e all have fun and parties.

Y   ou can sing and dance
E   veryone has lots of fun
A   dragon appears at the Chinese New Year
R   oaring like a lion.

Bushra Kausar (8)
Denbigh Junior School

THE SUN

The sun is a yellow ball in the sky
With eight hands
Children throw a ball up high
The sun gets a punch and hides behind the clouds
Her tears come down
She goes to sleep in her nice warm bed
And won't come out to play
So all day long it was as cool as a cucumber.

Rumi Begum (10)
Denbigh Junior School

WAR

Why do you hate each other?
Why do you fight?
Why do you kill each other?
Why destroy lives of the innocent?

Why do we have wars?
Why?

Sami Bronson (11)
Denbigh Junior School

HAIKU

The old woman waves
To her daughter who's leaving
She's alone again.

Bilal Khaliq (10)
Denbigh Junior School

FLOWERS

Flowers are nice - just like you
Flowers smell lovely - just like you
Flowers are sweet - just like you
Flowers are pretty - just like you
Flowers are beautiful - just like you
Flowers are super - just like you
Flowers sparkle - just like you!

Fareha Khanom (8)
Denbigh Junior School

JEALOUSY

Jealousy is the colour of green grass
Jealousy smells of old musty things
Jealousy tastes of blood.
Jealousy sounds like hateful words
Jealousy feels like the cut of a knife
Jealousy lives in the middle of hate.

Mariyah Chaudery (10)
Denbigh Junior School

CLOUDS

Clouds are loud
Grey and fluffy white clouds
Making thunder when it rains
Making a flood when the rain doesn't stop
Clouds!

Mahir Tajwar Alam (8)
Denbigh Junior School

THE BEACH

Stretched out sleepily in the shade
On a day when the sun's as fierce as a lion
I'm feeling really hot and sticky
And my face is beetroot-red.

The sea looks like the deep blue sky
As I head towards it for a swim
But the sand sucks my feet
Making me want to run as fast as Concorde.
I'm so glad to reach the water
I splash like a dolphin
The tiny waves welcome me like a king
And I felt as cold as ice.

Khashim Hussain (10)
Denbigh Junior School

CHRISTMAS

C   hristmas time is really fun
H   appy Christmas everyone
R   oasted turkey for you to eat
I   cing on the cake for a Christmas treat
S   eeing everyone is such fun
T   winkling lightS on the tree shine like the sun
M   ary's baby was born on this day
A   ngels knelt down and began to pray
S   anta brings presents for us to see

Merry Christmas for everyone from me.

Aroosa Hussain (8)
Denbigh Junior School

THE BEACH

Stretched out sleepily in the shade
On a day when the sun's as fierce as
                    a volcano
Shining on me
I'm feeling really hot and sticky
And my face is as red as human blood.

The sea looks as cool as ice to me
As I head towards it for a swim
But the sand makes my feet feel sticky
Sticky as if chewing gum were on me
Making me run as fast as I can.

I'm so glad to meet the water
I splash about as a dolphin would
Tiny waves welcome me by hugging
                    me tightly
They feel as if they love me.

Shaminah Miah (11)
Denbigh Junior School

AN ACROSTIC

M y mummy is beautiful and brave. She gives me my
U mbrella when it starts to rain.
M um cooks delicious spaghetti and
M eatballs for dinner. Sometimes she does things wrong, but
Y es! She's still the mum I know and love.

Danielle Siriboe (8)
Denbigh Junior School

MY BROTHER

Who put the worms in my bed?
Who threw a stink bomb in Dad's shed?
Who painted our cat's face rosy-red?
My brother.

Who put salt in the sugar pot?
Who left an apple in my bag to rot?
Who stuck a drawing pin in my boot?
My brother.

Who stuck a lolly in my hair?
Who pulled the eyes of my teddy bear?
Who put jelly on the chair?
My brother.

Who put all my toys in the bin?
Who kicked a football at my chin?
Who always moans when he doesn't win?
My brother.

Who hid Grandpa's new false teeth?
Who fed the dog with our roast beef?
Who gives Mum a lot of grief?

You'll never guess who . . .

My brother!

Rameez Khaliq (8)
Denbigh Junior School

WATERSPOUTS

The great towering fountain,
Tornadoes of water,
Sprouting from the sea,
Overruling the dark waters.

These creatures look like Nessie,
Come bringing terror to the people,
The power of a hurricane,
The size of a monster.

It gives no mercy,
Its icy blast throws many,
Throwing creatures of many sizes,
So now you know why it rains frogs.

The tornado winds,
Its massive strength,
Its torrents of rain,
Makes its name.

The lord of the seas,
A god almighty,
Trembles under its wrath,
So does the land,

The water tornado!

Thomas Bedford (10)
Edlesborough School

HIDDEN TREASURES

The sparkling jewels flashing in the hot sun
We've only just found them
It was hidden in the flaming hot sand
With an X spot on it.
There was an old shipwreck in the shining dazzling sea.
Look there are pirates on the high sea
Oh no! Hide the hidden treasures.
Remember to put an X spot over.
Quickly hide behind this tree
Look there is something in that tree.
Have a look . . . it's a map
But we have already found the glittering treasure
Quickly have a look
The pirates are coming!

Tamzin Mead (7)
Edlesborough School

HIDDEN TREASURE

We are evil pirates
We come from our creaky boat
We're skilful and cunning, like a fox.
We've come for the hidden treasure,
We will challenge you to a fight, if you dare.
The treasure is in there, but
There're traps in there too.
We're on the golden, hot sand
We will keep you hostage for a day or two.

Then next, I escaped, I got the treasure.
It's mine, all mine!

Patrick Marsh (7)
Edlesborough School

HIDDEN TREASURES

Bang, crash, dippy, wavy seas
We are fighting the pirates
Clang, clash, go the swords
The pirate's eye patch is deadly black.

We are trying not to fall
In the shark-infested water.
Yes! We win!
The pirate ship sinks.
Off we go to find the treasure,
Now we are on a rickety bridge,
'We're off afar,' we said
'We are going in a gloomy cave.'

There was a spot with an X
We dug the X and found some treasure.
'Hooray!'

Jack Rogers (8)
Edlesborough School

THE DRAGON

There was a terrible dragon who lived in a cage,
A very dark place.
Now the dragon was very cross, so he broke out of the cage.
He flew towards the city, the people saw him
They were terrified.
The army tried to stop the dragon,
But they didn't
So the dragon went away.

Joe Appleby (8)
Edlesborough School

HIDDEN TREASURES

We're digging,
We're in the deep, hot sand.
Where is the treasure map?
Wrapped in a band.
Where is the treasure?
Is it in a goldmine?
Is it in the sea?
I need more people to help me!
Oh look! Look I've found it.
Come and have a look!
Now we can find the treasure
At the top it says
'Look in a goldmine.'
We follow the map,
We've found the bolted padlock,
We need to find the key.
Let's go in further to see
What we can see
In the deep, dark, goldmine.
Was a gleaming key.
We grabbed it and zoomed back
'We're rich! I tell you, rich!'

Christine Salmon (8)
Edlesborough School

HIDDEN TREASURES

Underneath the gleaming hot sand
is our hidden treasure.
It's ours, now we have the
golden treasure.
Good old map!

If it wasn't for my mum . . .
I was very near to my treasure.
She woke me up, right near
the raging stream.
As I was about to jump in
to fulfil my dreams.

Bethany Bilton (7)
Edlesborough School

HIDDEN TREASURES

Fortunes of treasure hidden somewhere,
Gold and silver out there,
Somewhere, waiting to be found.
Over the seas we go, searching for shipwrecks and caves.
X marks the spot.
'Wait! We've hit something.'
'What is it?'
'It's a shipwreck.'
'A rusty old shipwreck' they all called out.
They swam inside and took a look . . .
There was nothing there.
Wait a minute!
There's a bright light coming from that door!
It's glistening treasure!
Rubies, gold, pearls and diamonds.
We took it to the ship and sailed back home.
The chest was too heavy,
We had to drop it into the sea.
'There goes our treasure.'
At the end of our journey, we told our mums
About our swashbuckling adventure.

James Smart (7)
Edlesborough School

HIDDEN TREASURES

Hidden treasure, hidden treasure,
Is there a hidden treasure?
Did I just get this crumbly
Old map for nothing?

It was a long adventure
Fighting evil pirates.
Swimming in the dangerous seas,
Then I found the X marked
On the spot.
Wow! It was a treasure chest.
It wasn't easy to carry,
Making me very weary.
Sweat pouring, getting tired and sleepy.
Before I knew it, I was screaming
For help!

I felt a comforting hand on my head
Saying 'It's time to wake up precious!'
It was Mum, she's a special treasure but
Not the gold and silver kind.

Heather Mullett (7)
Edlesborough School

EGYPT

In the night sky, the
Mummies rise up

The eyes shone bright
Red, like flames, Egypt
Cats purred for the
Whole night.

Kieran Viljoen (8)
Edlesborough School

HIDDEN TREASURES

Over the seas on a foggy night
I started my trip to find the amazing sight.
The map is too old but
I am told
To follow my dream.

It wasn't easy to seek my dream,
Heavy seas and cruel weather.

But then I stumbled on the enormous
Sparkling key.
To unlock my treasure, I had to dive
Under the sea.

What a sight!
Dazzling precious stones,
Hidden by the sea.

Andrew Scott-Lewis (7)
Edlesborough School

THE TREASURE

We're going to seek our fortune, and drink lots of rum,
We're going to find our treasure, and fill up my tum.
We're going to see the mermaids, and Long John Silver.
We're going to a shipwreck, then eat all the dinner.
We're going on a ship, and drink the coffee,
We're going down under the ocean, and the Mediterranean Sea.
We're going to see the hot sand, and the blazing sun,
We're going to find some valuables, then home to Mum.

Sabrina Calloway (10)
Edlesborough School

HIDDEN TREASURES

In the wavy sea,
There was a raging storm,
We saw a pirate ship.
Fighting for our life
We are both heading
For the same sight.

Over on the island
It was a race to
Find our pleasure.
The hidden treasure.
Cunning pirates
Were not far behind.
It wasn't night,
But we had to fight.

It was a close shave,
But we made it to the other shore.
Now we have the pleasure
Of the *hidden treasures.*

Joshua Taylor (7)
Edlesborough School

HIDDEN TREASURES

Deep down in an old shipwreck
Under the deep, gloomy sea
Stood some evil pirates
With piercing eyes

'The treasure's all mine!'
I jumped out of nowhere.
'You can't get the hidden treasure,
I've got the crumpled map
With the X marked spot on
No one can stop me, except me!'

'I've got the hidden treasure
And here it is!
Sparkling and gleaming silver jewels
Crystal and diamonds all around.
As for you evil pirates . . . good boy.'

Hannah Fox (7)
Edlesborough School

HIDDEN TREASURES

Hidden treasures
which can be found.
What shall I do?
Shall I dig beneath
the dirty ground?

What shall I do?
Shall I find the
dirty pirates?
They will lead
me to the place.

What shall I do?
Dive in the
dangerous sea?

Hidden treasures
might be found,
Hidden treasures
are not found by me.
Hidden treasures
are found by me.

Charlotte Ellis (7)
Edlesborough School

HIDDEN TREASURES

We are looking in a goldmine
for hidden treasures.
Under the sea, we
found our pleasure.
I found the treasure
But I could also see
Shivery killer sharks
With teeth like sparks
Heading straight for us.

I jumped and screamed
And everyone dreamed.
I think he has gone off for his lunch,
But I think not.
They snapped and roared at the boat
But guess what? I was afloat.
I went to the surface
I ran to the sand
It was hot, and that's where I stop!

Sebastian Calloway (7)
Edlesborough School

MY TREASURE

As I walked into my new garden,
I felt dew coming through my socks and shoes,
I saw bluebells and daisies all around me,
I thought, this is my treasure.

I walked deeper into my garden,
I saw a wonderful high climbing frame,
And swings which could take you as high
As you wanted to go.
I thought, this is my treasure.

When I look up into the sky,
I can see a light shade of blue,
Covering all of the gardens, houses and flats.
I can see birds flying over my head,
And butterflies fluttering overhead.
I thought, this is definitely my treasure.

Melissa Maria Wade (9)
Edlesborough School

HIDDEN TREASURES

We're in a fierce storm
fighting the evil pirates,
To find the precious map.
Their weapons were deadly,
We fought all the way.

We found the map in the smelly dressing room,
The mission was under way.
There was a small hitch
We fell in a ditch.

After escaping the ditch,
The map took us to the burning desert
gasping for a drink.
We drank from the Nile,
set up camp and said
'Night, night!'

In the morning, the treasure
was revealed.
We took it to the museum
and in return we got
£50,000,000, so we'd
Completed our exciting mission.

Jack Coates (7)
Edlesborough School

The Sea, The Sand, The Sun

The sea, the sand, the sun can be
ever so much fun, you can meet the orange clippers
which clip the sand,
which reminds me of
Oh yeah! The spikes from the sun.

The sea, the sand, the sun can be
ever so much fun, you can get all sweaty and
sticky. Which should remind you that the sea
can be sweaty, and the sand can be
sticky stuff.
So remember, the sea, the sand
The sun can be
Ever so much fun
Oh yeah!

Kimberly Squire (8)
Edlesborough School

Hidden Treasures

Deep in dangerous seas
we are looking for a treasure chest.

It is ours now, we have found the shipwreck,
We go down to get the treasure, but no,
the pirates have made it too.
'Hey!' we say 'this belongs to us,
you see, we have the key!'

It wasn't easy fighting the evil pirates,
they weren't prepared to flee.
In the end it wasn't worth a fight,
so we went home and had a cup of tea.

Toby West (7)
Edlesborough School

FIRE

I keep people warm and cook people's food,
I am needed in winter when times get cold,
I am hated in summer when everything gets hot,
People dislike my heat and want to get away,
But . . .
I am the ruler, the indestructible threat,
I turn wood into ash and leaves into air,
I am the one who people can't stand,
They run and flee at the sound of my name.
My favourite victims are forests and woods,
They sizzle and crack into black, flaky dust,
My worst enemy is water,
It burns me down to my fate until I am no more.
I am fire.

Ben Evans (11)
Edlesborough School

HIDDEN TREASURE

Where no one dares to wander
I stand there and ponder
About a holy grail where nobody seeks
I stand in shadows for weeks and weeks
Wondering what lurks beneath
How do I think such grief
Will I find the sacred grail?
Is there such a grail, my determination leads a trail
Through cobwebs and traps plus cracks
They will leave such dangerous tracks
But I will live to tell the tale
of the
holy grail.

Christopher Mortimer (10)
Edlesborough School

HIDDEN TREASURES

Deep, deep down in the deep, blue sea,
was a shipwreck to see.
In the shipwreck was sparkling,
dazzling treasure.
The treasure belongs to the
nasty pirates on the sea.

The bronze and the silver
they all belonged to me.
Me, me, me only me!
I hid the treasure from
the pirates, only to lose
it again, to the sea.

It all fell into the stormy sea,
To be discovered again,
One day, by me.

Charlotte Holmes (7)
Edlesborough School

THE LIFETIME OF HIDDEN TREASURES

In the shimmering ocean,
Glorious fishes swam round a dazzling treasure box.
Inside it was gold which shone in the blazing hot sun.
Silver rings with diamonds and bronze cups.
Blue jewels, which shine in the moonlight,
Silky cobwebs which stick to you
When you try and take some treasure.

Gemma Yearley (8)
Edlesborough School

TREASURE

I opened the chest
A blinding light shone,
I put my hand into the chest
And pulled out gold!

We all cheered 'Hip, hip, hooray!'
Then the boat jerked
'Ahh!' I screamed.
As the gold flew into the sea.

A fish jumped up and swallowed the gold,
And dived back in with a *splash!*
I saw the ripples in the water
As the fish swam under the boat.

Then I saw a tidal wave coming
The whole crew screamed and went ballistic
'Run for your life!' I screamed
As the tidal wave came over the boat.
The treasure was gone!

Adam Lewis (9)
Edlesborough School

THE SEA

Under the sea is a wonderful place,
Where the bubbles dazzle as they rise.
The fish all glistening as they swim by,
The octopuses hiding in dark hollow holes.
The people who are snorkelling say
'Under the sea is a wonderful place.'

Anna Dean (8)
Edlesborough School

HIDDEN TREASURES

I'm on a wooden ship
We are off to find
Hidden treasure.

Is it in the murky goldmine
Or under the gloomy sea?
Let's go to the goldmine.
Hey! Here's some gold
Let's bring it back with us.
We'll go to the spooky cave.
Hey! I've found something.
We'll dig here . . . a map!
It says we need to go to the sea,
We've found the treasure.
We did it!

Joe Ashman (7)
Edlesborough School

SEA LIFE

Under the seaweed and through the waves
Far under the land where I sit.
Beyond the rainbow, where seagulls fly,
Stranger than any creature in the sea,
Its long frisky whiskers
And small rapid teeth,
Its rounded nose hides under the reef,
Yes, you might find it funny, you might find it weird
But it will gobble you up, at a frightening speed.
Yes, you might find it funny, you might find it weird.
But believe me it will eat you up at lightning speed!

Catherine Allen (8)
Edlesborough School

HIDDEN TREASURES

If it wasn't for my friends
I would be sitting at home,
eating my tea.
He dragged me into the woods,
to see something good.

He had an old map
which he discovered by accident
He seems to think it will lead us
to a golden treat.

It was difficult to follow the map,
it led us into a trap.

I wish I was at home, eating my tea.

Thomas Pratt (7)
Edlesborough School

THE FLYAWAY PLANE

I made a paper aeroplane
and threw it through the air.
It landed in the water
and it was stranded there.
I went to find my rubber boots,
so I could paddle there,
but when I went to fetch it,
it wasn't anywhere.
I put my hand in the water,
it was as cold as ice.
All I found was an aluminium can,
which wasn't very nice!

Daniel J Law (9)
Edlesborough School

THINGS I LOVE

I like lots of sound,
The sounds of people when they are found.
Here are some sounds which I love,
The sound of the cooing dove
And the sound of dolphins in the waves
Children yelling in the caves.

I like touching things
Especially feathery wings.
The cold ice cream
Makes lots of people scream.
The fur on the cat
And the rough, cool mat.

I like smelling
Things which people are selling.
Salmon and chips
Are nice with dips,
Bony fish
Which grant a wish.

Elizabeth Ranson (9)
Edlesborough School

THE LOST TREASURES

Sailing in the boat
Through the turquoise water,
Towards the golden sand
Beneath the swaying palm trees.

The map in my hand
Old and worn
Excited but scared
Treasures to be found?

I'm digging in the sand,
I feel something hard.
I'm opening the chest.
Oh no! A bone!
A dog had got here before me!

Stephanie Holmes (9)
Edlesborough School

HIDDEN TREASURES

I'm on an adventure, swimming through
the deep dangerous sea towards a great big ship.
I climb up the rope ladder, but to my
surprise, ten fierce faces are waiting, just for me.
I try to dodge them, but no luck at all,
I was stuck outside in dreary weather,
getting wetter and wetter, but then
I see some doors leading to a cabin,
with a bright lamp.
I do a backwards flip over them and run.

When I arrive, I take a quick snack and
run to the next creaky wooden door,
but this time it is a floorboard,
I open it with a slight crack, down there
it was pitch-black and I felt my way around.
The pirates are near now, I quietly hide,
when they were in, they somehow turned a light on
I come out from hiding and use my sword against them.
I cut all their heads off and in a blinding light,
I see a golden chest, I open it and what a sight!
Alleluia!

Jack Blumsom (7)
Edlesborough School

Hidden Treasures

There I am on a ship
I'm in my deep, deep sleep.
I fight the evil pirates,
I chop off their heads
I steal the map and jump
Into the shark-infested water.

I hit the sharks on the head
with the map,
Swim to shore, safe at last.
X marks the spot.

I dig deep, deep down
in the sand.
I see something shining
It's the key to the treasure,
It's for me, for me!

I jump into the shark-infested water
once again then swim to safety.
The treasure lights up the sky,
I can see below the sky,
But oh no! I feel something is
grabbing me. Aah! (Morning)
Mum says 'Don't scream!
It's okay, you can have fun today!'

Abigail Rose O'Connell (7)
Edlesborough School

MORNING AT THE SEASIDE

The sun is rising up
The birds begin to sing,
The ice cream man is getting ready
To sell his ice creams.
The sea is very calm,
And the sand is nice and warm.
The fish are as still as statues,
It is the same every morning.

The seaside in the morning, is a lovely sight,
Only two people sunbathing and swimming,
Only five people playing.

The pebbles in the sea,
The seaweed on the sand.
The jellyfish swims around
The rocks, so heavy, you can't lift them
And pale blue, so pretty.

Still no one at the seaside,
The sun is still shining.
Nothing has changed,
Until people jump into the water.
There are so many people here.
I love the seaside!

Vicki York (9)
Edlesborough School

A WINDY DAY

On a windy day
The horses stay
On the farm
Then they run away.

Trees wobble and sway,
It's just their way.
The animals hide
From the windy day.

The rain lashes down
On a windy day.
The waves crash around
But the mice make no sound.

The sun comes out,
The rain goes away.
The horses all
Come back to play

But it is still a windy day.

Dominic Russell (9)
Edlesborough School

TORNADO

There like an elephant's trunk,
Grey and long while shaking furiously,
It streams through the air like an eagle,
It moves across the land at the speed of light,
Nothing stands in its way.

Its powers are indestructible,
It brushes away everything like a huge duster,
No one can stand their ground,
The victims of it are thrown for miles.

Its structure is amazing,
It's an arm with no bones,
Swaying in the air,
A huge natural disaster.

The tornado.

Adam Sears (10)
Edlesborough School

HIDDEN TREASURES

The hidden treasures of the ocean
Come not in big brown boxes
Locked with many locks
But in the shining waters covering our planet.

The ocean is home to many animals
From tiny scarlet prawns to huge blue whales,
Right down to the seabed,
Living a private life.

In colder areas of sea
Icebergs float like boats,
Huge chunks of land ice
Floating around on their own.

Tides are coming in and out
Never getting tired,
Coming in then withdrawing
Leaving miles of open space.

The water glistens for miles and miles
In moonlight then in sun.
Without searching for them
We find the ocean's treasures.

Rachael Evans (11)
Edlesborough School

HIDDEN TREASURES

Down beneath the deep, deep sea
There was an old and weary shipwreck.
In there were strange swimming pirates
Clapping skeleton bones.

Shipwreck guarded by the sharks
I carefully swam through
The great white teeth.

In a sweet smelling room
Was the staring treasure
I brought it back from fierce seas.

Hidden, hidden, hidden treasure
It was not the hidden treasure anymore,
It has been found by me!

Ian Brown (8)
Edlesborough School

HIDDEN TREASURE

Where no one dares to wander
I stand and ponder
About a holy grail
Not just a grail, the sacred grail
If there's such a grail there must be a trail
To what I ponder and dream about
Through cobwebs and traps and long cracks
There I leave small foot tracks
But will I live to tell the tale
    Of the
        Sacred holy grail.

William Morgan (10)
Edlesborough School

SEASONS

A spring day and a new beginning,
No frosty morns or tobogganing.
A spring day with April showers,
No auburn leaves or dying flowers.

A summer's day of burning heat,
No sudden rain or cold, damp feet.
A summer's day with water gun fights,
No blankets of snow or chilly nights.

An autumn day with golden trees,
No sunshine or buzzy bees.
An autumn day with conkers hidden in prickly coats,
No summer cruises or trips on boats.

A winter's day so full of fog,
No one playing or walking the dog.
A winter's day in bed with flu,
No fluffy clouds or skies so blue.

Alex Marsh (10)
Edlesborough School

HIDDEN TREASURES

In the wavy sea we are trying to find
the hidden map.
The pirates were far too clever to reach
the map before us.
We had to fight the naughty pirates
so that we could reach our goal.
We found the treasures and
we had lots of pleasure.

Jessica Turner (7)
Edlesborough School

SNOW DAY TREASURES

S till snowing outside
N othing's going to show up at night,
O nly going to snow.
W hite snow is better than any water flow.

D aylight's coming
A hoy, with the plumbing
Y es, yes! I've found some treasure.

T reasure, treasure, I love this weather
R ings, rings
E xcellent strings.
A ll wonderful things,
S uch a beautiful person sings,
U mbrellas, umbrellas
R eally such a terrible necklace, terrible.
E ggs, eggs, beautiful things
S uch a terrible finger, it sings.

Lauren Yearley (8)
Edlesborough School

THE SEASIDE

S ee the sea, see the sun
E lla my friend is coming with me,
A friend is coming with me.
S ee the sand, see the sea
I ce creams. 'Can I have one Dad?'
D ad says 'No!' I go into a mood
E lla says 'Don't worry, ask Mum.'

It's fun at the seaside!

Hannah Mustoe (8)
Edlesborough School

SNOWING

S till snowing outside,
N othing much left,
O nly snow.
W hite all over,
I nside's boring,
N ever outside.
G o outside and it's snowing!

O utside's wonderful,
U p in the sky;
T he little drops of
S now tumble to the ground.
I nside's warm,
D addy's coming home
E verybody's happy;
   It's snowing.

Beth Mercer (8)
Edlesborough School

HIDDEN TREASURE

T reasure is rare,
R iddles are annoying,
E aten people are in sharks' bellies,
A crobatic skills will get me to my target,
S uccess is brilliant,
U gly creatures are horrid,
R atty sharks are beastly and annoying,
E lephant seals are everywhere.

Sam Blumsom (9)
Edlesborough School

HIDDEN TREASURES

Hidden treasures, hidden treasures everywhere,
Deep down in the salty ocean
lies a rotten old shipwreck.
We go down, down, down
into the shipwreck we go.
We see a box, rotten and wet,
we open the horrid box and
to our surprise, see gold,
silver, bronze and pearls,
dazzling in the sun.

I go up, up, up into the air,
when I'm up, I say to myself
I must keep it a secret
I get the box and bring it up,
it dazzles in the bright sun.
I go home, I have to keep it safe,
I put it under my bed so that
if anybody wants it, they have to
get the map from me,
which marks the spot.

Eve Greenow (7)
Edlesborough School

007

James Bond smashed open the window with his suitcase,
He tied the man up with a piece of string.
He jumped out of the window,
The man skidded along the floor.
And banged his head on the window.
James Bond went to the headquarters.

Oliver Howard (8)
Edlesborough School

SKULL BONES

My bones are cold
They're rotten with mould
I spoiled my life
With a sharp, sharp knife
I've been here for years
I've been through fears

I've frightened loads of people
I've scared one with a needle
My bones are slimy
My head's all grimy
I live in a cave
I am jolly brave

It smells of eggs
And rotten cheese
It's so cold
You think you'll freeze
I don't eat any food
And I never get in a mood!

Christopher Scott-Lewis (9)
Edlesborough School

MONSTERS EVERYWHERE

Monsters, monsters everywhere
Some big, some small, some tiny, some tall.
Some thin, some fat, some old and bold,
Some purple, some blue, some green, some white,
Monsters everywhere,
So beware, so beware, so beware!

Matthew Audouard (8)
Edlesborough School

THE SEA, THE SEA

The sea, the sea is a wonderful place
To be, to be the mystical place. The sea, the sea
The sea, the walking away sea, Oh why
Why do you walk away sea. Sea, I see the sea
I see you, the you, you, oh you, my no
My no, no, no. The sea is the sea. That's
Why it is my sea, but why
But why does it want to walk away so, so
The sea, the sea, a wonderful place to be
For me to see on and forever, forever, to
to, to, to, to see.

The sea, sea

To be for me.

Alex Mack (8)
Edlesborough School

THERE'S A GHOST ON THE PAGE

There's a ghost on the page
He is white
He has frightened people out of the book
He is very, very scary!
Eeek!!
Rats don't scare him, nothing does.

Monsters try to get him out of the poem
But the ghost wins
He's never lost
Not in a hundred years
So don't try
Ever!

Ryan Sears
Edlesborough School

THANK YOU

Thank you for the times we share
Thank you for being there
When things are going bad
Thank you for that shoulder to rest on
When I'm sad.

When I receive a letter
It makes me feel a lot better
Deep down inside
You are the one
My very true friend.

When we meet I feel like a cheat
And sometimes it feels
Like we're walking down
A different street
So I would like to take this chance to say
Thank you!

Thomas Howard (8)
Edlesborough School

FRUIT

Fruit, sweet mangoes, bananas and strawberries too,
Come on and eat them, they're good for you!

Fruit, sweet kiwis, grapes and apples too,
They're all for you!

Fruit, sweet, marvellous fruit,
It's all around you, can't you see?
And it's waiting for you!

Kayli Shaw (9)
Edlesborough School

WEATHER

The wind and rain has come again,
It's cold and wet here.

It's hot and sunny
A good place
To get a suntan.

There is thunder,
There is lightning.
It is loud and
Very frightening.

The fluffy clouds are
Out to play
Like candyfloss,
They float away.

Sarah Green (8)
Edlesborough School

THE BADGER

I had found a bin,
I looked in,
I saw a few bitten biscuits,
Half a sandwich,
It was night so I had to be quiet.
I ate until morning fell,
I snuck under the bed
And I hid under some clothes
And some socks!

Rebecca Thorne (9)
Edlesborough School

THE BIG, FLUFFY BUNNY

There's a big, fluffy bunny
In the garden next to me
It hops along the grass
Which is very funny to see

It leaps and jumps in the air
As if it's trying to fly
I wish that I could be like him
I can't, but I'll have a try

I think that he is really cute
I wish that he was mine
I'll save up all my money
And I'll buy a bunny, just as fine.

Gemma Paine (8)
Edlesborough School

HIDDEN TREASURE

As I walked along the beach that day
I realised my mum had passed away
My dad had died
A little tear formed inside.
I walked along to my cabin
Found a letter on my bed
It read,
Come and see me I am lost without you
So I went
Packed my stuff
Went to the bus
I saw my aunt at last
We hugged each other.

Charlotte Squire (11)
Edlesborough School

TREASURE, TREASURE

Treasure, treasure
Tucked underground,
Waiting to be found
By pirates, explorers or miners.
It's waiting, it's waiting.

Wherever it is, it's there,
Under the leaves, rocks or ground.
Waiting to be found,
It could be buried, near you now,
It's waiting, it's waiting.

Wrapped in paper or in a chest,
Locked with a golden key,
Waiting to be found,
Wrapped in soil, which you have to dig.
It's waiting, it's waiting.

It may have been there for many years,
It may be either big or small.
Waiting to be found,
It may be new, it may be old,
It's waiting, it's waiting.

What fun to make a sandcastle,
Nick loves his summer holiday
It's almost found,
An old biscuit tin holding treasures within.
It's found! It's found!

Christopher Wright (8)
Edlesborough School

ALL ABOUT ME

My name is Joshua Eastham
And I am eight years old.
I live in a little village called Northall
And here the weather is cold.

I meet my friends in the playground
I say 'Hello!'
We play football, until the bell goes.

English is my favourite subject
Maths is my second choice.
Singing I like
But I haven't got a very big voice.

At lunchtime I play football
With Chris and Joe
Because there is nowhere
Else to go.

At 3.20 I go home
And have a cup of tea.
I like this bit best
    Because it's just um
And me!

At 8 o'clock at night
I mustn't make a peep,
And when Mum comes up
I pretend to be asleep.

Joshua Eastham (9)
Edlesborough School

THE RICH MAN AND THE POOR MAN

The rich man
Nose in the air
Strutting around
With an all snooty look.

The poor man
Huddled in a corner
Creeping around
Face hidden.

The rich man
Dressed so finely
Flawless
In a lovely coat.

The poor man
Dressed in rags,
Tattered and torn
No shoes.

The rich man
A fine feast every day
Scraps for the dogs
Half-finished plates.

The poor man
Begging for food
Each day
A crumb for each meal.

Catherine Quinlan (9)
Edlesborough School

YOU CAN

You can laugh
Your head off if
You must.
I only fell asleep
On the coach and snored.

You can go bright
Red if you dare.
I only had a bad hair
Day on the television.

You can stamp
And punch the floor
I only wrote a
Five page story
Upside down.

You can fall on the
Floor if you really care.
I only went to school
With odd shoes on.
You can, you can . . .

But wait . . .
Isn't that jam
On your nose?
Ha, ha!

Clare Everson (8)
Edlesborough School

HIDDEN TREASURE

Round the corridor, up the stairs
I've come to see the old, straight face
Not a smile but a frown I see
I thought he'd have that silly smirk upon his hard and stony face
Like last time.

But a lot has changed since last time
For now I'm not at his sweet-smelling bungalow
But at the original plain hospital
Lying there at his bedside
He's very ill you know - cancer!

I think of the time when we played
Just Grandad and me
But he'll be gone in some hours' time
His face and the enjoyable memories
They'll stay in me until the day I die.

Suddenly a nurse runs in
Something's wrong with Grandad
The nurse asks me to wait outside
I walk off slowly and backwards
Only to see a sky blue curtain being drawn.

I go and buy an ice-cold can of Coke
I take sips but I can't help but think of him
And soon the same nurse who asked me to leave
Tells me to go in, so I do
He's just lying there, picking at the grapes.

I fear what will happen
Thoughts scroll through my mind
But one pops up and says
I'll say it 'I love you'
A lovely sweet smile is unleashed upon his face.

Olivia Rust
Edlesborough School

DAYS OF THE WEEK

On Monday there's maths,
English comes next
Science is last
Monday is glum day.

Tuesday is sleeping
We sleep on our desks,
I close one eye
Tuesday is snooze day.

Wednesday is new,
Fashion, CDs, games
Get in the trend
Wednesday is trend day.

Thursday is when we use greenery,
In a project on growing.
But snails and worms join in
Thursday is worm day.

Friday is when we say bye to our friends,
Until Monday comes again.
Call me on your mobile on Saturday,
Friday is bye-bye day.

Saturday is when the cat comes in,
Ready for its dinner.
With mice in its mouth, whilst coming in the door,
Saturday is *cater*day

Sunday is when we want to have fun.
Playing games, singing and running along,
Just remember the days of the week
Sunday is fun day.

Jack Davies (8)
Edlesborough School

THE RED MOUSE IN THE BLACK HOUSE

The mouse in the
House is a red tiny
Mouse and he owns a
Black huge house.
He is small, he is
Creepy and he owns a
Black huge house.

And the red mouse from the
Black house, is as brave as anything.

In comes a ghost of
The ghouls and goblins with
All his other friends.
He is the meanest, he is
The scariest and he kills anyone.

And the red mouse from the
Black house, is as brave as anything.

Bianca Hicks (8)
Edlesborough School

THE HIDDEN TREASURE

In the dark, gloomy cave, a spider had
Spun a very spiky web.
Under the web was a hole just
Big enough for me.
I came out and the sand was in front of me
And blowing on to me.
I felt like going on the sea, so I did.

I got a boat and was swept out to sea,
An enormous wave swept me under,
I saw a cross and fell down a hole.
I suddenly saw a glimpse of gold,
It was the hidden treasure,
I had found it . . . the treasure!

Olivia Berry (8)
Edlesborough School

NOISES AND MOVEMENTS

The banging on the window
The smashing of the door,
The footsteps of a person
The cracking of the floor.

The rustling of the bushes,
The singing of birds which fly,
As quiet as a hedgehog,
The rainy clouds in the sky.

The swaying of a tree,
A moaning person shouting,
The crying of a baby,
A noisy person on an outing.

The light on a torch,
The sound that the wind makes,
The shooting of a gun,
The crumbling of some flakes.

The engine of a car,
The flashing of a flashlight.
No ghosts in the daytime,
They only come out at night.

Joseph Bradley (8)
Edlesborough School

I Am The Wind

I am the wind
lonely and sad
independent as a hawk
as stubborn as a mule.

Chorus:
If only I was the wolf
Who travelled in a pack.

I've travelled through the rainforest
I've searched in the sea
for a proper caring
loving *family!*

Chorus:
If only I was the wolf
Who travelled in a pack.

I have asked the rain
I've pleaded with the lightning
but I guess I am alone!

Jonathan Costello (9)
Edlesborough School

The Bully

I walk to the playground
I see the bully, his fists large and round.
I'm trying to avoid him
But my thoughts are rather grim.

He throws at me a large fist
To dodge it, I must twist,
He throws at me a punching slam,
I'm trying to dodge it, but *wham!*

He walks off all alone,
Pleased with the punches he's thrown.
Today is windy, I see the flag on a pole,
So does the bully, but he slips
And falls in a hole.

Conor Marum (8)
Edlesborough School

DOWN IN THE JUNGLE

Deep in the jungle on the tallest trees,
Swing some chattering monkeys.
You can see them move in
Groups or in families.

From up in the sky, you hear a call,
Its coat is jet black with a
Few colours glowing.
It swoops and it swirls all
Over the sky,
What can it be . . . but a *toucan!*

Splish, splash, there's a waterfall over there,
It's got a rock pool at the bottom.
As the water falls, it lands
With a piercing *splash!*

Down on the ground, as far
As you can get,
Lies a snake, hissing so loud.
It's getting ready to pounce
On a poor little mouse.
Its back is a dark green with red spots,
Watch out! It's coming this way!
Run!

Sarah Thompson (9)
Edlesborough School

THE DRAGON

As I threw a dusty rock into the river,
A sleek, golden eagle took flight from inside a
slime-covered cave.
I wandered ever nearer to the cavern and touched
the vine covered wall.

I entered and stared as I lingered around the mouth
of the cave.
Creatures that only exist in fairy tales sprang out
at me,
I began to run, further into the forbidden grotto.

I stopped and there, staring at me was a fire-breathing
dragon,
It opened its mouth, as if it was about to roar,
I expected a flame, like lava, bubbling and burning,
But instead it just snapped at me and flew off into the
sun's golden rays.
I was alone, very alone.

I started walking away, my shoes scuffing along the
ground,
I saw many other mystical creatures which looked like
they wanted to be my friend,

But I liked the dragon best!
I got lost and started to cry, but then my wonderful dragon
swooped down and lifted me onto its back,

It was like a dream, up above, as if I was riding the
fluffy, silver clouds,
The dragon's scales, as hard as stone and as cold as ice.

Its breath lingering around me,
Its eyes shining and glowing,

I wished I could stay forever,
But one day it flew off and never came back.

Emily Knight (11)
Edlesborough School

THE JAGUAR HUNT

I'm entering the jungle,
The trees like walls,
There is enough vegetation to hide a small building,
It definitely will be hard to spot the jaguar.

We have no intention to kill,
But only to see this fearful beast
In its natural home.
I have heard the close encounter stories,
I don't want anything like that to happen today
(Gulp).

It will be hard; the jaguar we are following
Has been known to travel up to 5km in one day.
Usually jaguars are very lazy, but they can turn active
Like this one.
Phew, what a long way to travel.

Then we saw it just a few metres away,
We backed off; any sane person would,
What a magnificent sight, its spots like rosettes,
It yawned and stretched, just like a domestic cat,
As it sauntered off into the jungle, we rejoiced,
Our efforts had paid off.

James Lake (11)
Edlesborough School

SEASONS

The year begins with a sulky, dismal sky
bearing a coy sun selfishly lurking behind ashen clouds.
Tears of sorrow often gush from above
drenching the still bare trees.

As spring approaches the rain hastens, cascading down,
drowning the growing grass.
But when spring is in its full glory all the gloom seems worth it;
a burst of golden sunlight, framed by the hazy, violet sky.
The trees are blanketed in a faint pink blossom
and birds are frantically making nests in which to raise their young.
Baby animals are taking their first peep into the wide world,
while their mother lays exhausted in the hay.

Spring soon fades and dead blossom carpets the ground,
the trees replace the pink buds with crisp, green leaves.
Summer is here and so is the sun!
The golden rays of light are set off by the vivid aqua sky.
Golden beaches are riddled with tanned holidaymakers,
leisurely building castles and towers from hot sand.
The heat is so immense; grass wilts and people sweat,
but even summer must come to an end.

Gradually the wind breaks in and blows away the burning heat.
The leaves begin to shrivel and soon the colour changes.
Autumn has arrived and the dazzling colours with it!
The harsh wind soon blows all the crunchy leaves to the ground.
Rain tips continuously down,
making the leaves below slimy and sludgy.

The rain becomes snow, softly dancing in the breeze.
Winter has just appeared and so have Christmas decorations.
It is so cold outside, the only sign of life is a frosty snowman
staring emptily into space.

Icicles hang from condensation-coated windows
as baubles dangle from the tree.
Christmas drifts dreamily by and the year ends in a shimmering
veil of snow.

Lucy Brooks (11)
Edlesborough School

THE FOREST MOUSE

As a mouse scuttles through a gloomy forest
The shining moon reflects in her glittering eyes
Not a rustle of a crispy, brown leaf as she walks by
Her tail flicking in the bitter, dark night air

She catches glimpses of other midnight creatures
Like an owl, its eyes wide and alert for danger
A hedgehog through the foggy mist of the trees
Even a sly and cunning fox waiting to pounce

She carries on, halting to any minute sound
The trees becoming spookier and darker as she goes
The deepest part of the forest showing its magic
This forest was becoming a maze of trees

She turns frantically to see an owl swooping behind
The owl, eyes alight, hooting softly
She runs for her life, tail close to the ground
Until the hooting slowly fades into the dusk

At last she finds where she wants to be
The edge of the mystical forest
Where the sunset makes her silhouette
Where on the grass, dew sparkles.

Natasha Hopgood (10)
Edlesborough School

TUTANKHAMUN'S TOMB

As I strolled through the dusty pyramid
I smelt a foul and disgusting smell
I felt the dust and dirt clench at my throat so tightly
I entered a room, so colourful
Its walls were filled with hieroglyphs so well preserved
Each picture so neatly painted on, in colours of the natural world.

I quietly left the room.

The smell was getting worse
I must be getting nearer the rotting carcass
I entered the second room to find a body
So neatly wrapped in muslin bandages
I walked closer to the body, identified as the King Tutankhamun.
All his possessions scattered on an old wooden table,
A lock of creamy blond hair, a slate covered in hieroglyphs
And an axe covered in golden leaves.

I quietly left the room.

I entered the third room to find two other rotting bodies,
But I thought that the tomb was only Tutankhamun's.
I read the beautifully painted hieroglyphs to find out
That his only two daughters had been killed and buried
To rest with their father.

I quietly left the room.

I stood in silence, staring at the two bodies still in coffins
Of great colours, gold, silver and bronze.

I quietly left the room to find the entrance of the tomb.

Lauren Suddaby (11)
Edlesborough School

THE GOBI DESERT

As I walk across the boiling summer sands,
Burning my bare feet as I peacefully stroll,
With hot sand flowing in and out of my toes
And the sun burning my back,
Dying of thirst,
Trying to take my mind off my hunger and need of drink,
I see something, as I come closer it becomes clearer.
A *lake!* I run up to it and bend down to wash my face.
Suddenly I do not feel cold, fresh water splashing on my face
But gritty things.
Looking down there is nothing, nothing but hot sand
Gleaming gold in the sunlight.
I realise it is a mirage.
Apart from the sand and me, the desert is clear, or so I think,
Maybe a bit of wildlife, but a strange noise occurs
And I find myself quickly looking around.
'W-who's there?' I stutter quietly.
There it is again, but this time it is a lot clearer, now a sort of hiss.
I feel a scaly touch on my leg, I give a quiet yell.
As I look down, I see a snake coiling itself around my ankles.
Now I am running as fast as can be, then stop for a rest on a rock.
What do I see now, a plant, a cactus, I reach out and feel,
'Ouch,' I figure it is real.
Suddenly I feel colder, much colder, but it is not dark.
I have run into winter, I quickly jog on the spot and rub my hands.
I get tighter and tighter,
Suddenly I am being squeezed by a snake and get bitten.
Then I wake up, snuggled up warm in my bed.

Jessica McMahon (11)
Edlesborough School

THE SPOOKY RAINFOREST

Once there was a rainforest
No one went there,
The adults said it's all spooky
And they wouldn't dare to go there.
I'm now on an aeroplane, gliding through the sky
Oh crash, boom, bash!

Oh no! We've just crashed in a river,
I splashed across the river, strong and bold,
And there was the spooky rainforest.
I stepped closer, *I can't go in!* I said to myself.
I heard a trembling voice, I stepped right back
I was scared to death, then I heard a voice say
'You're going to be late!'
After it came the scary part, but
I realised it was just a dream.

Lucy McMahon (8)
Edlesborough School

THE BADGER

There was a badger who lived in the house
The badger sat on the bed all day.
At night the badger came to life
He had made his den to sleep in
He made it from socks and clothes
When I woke I'd lost the badger
I looked under the bed
I found him, I said,
'Come here big badger.'

Alex Taylor (9)
Edlesborough School

MY BABY SISTER

My baby sister has a round, red nose,
And a round, tubby belly
She has ten tiny toes
But she can get quite smelly.

When she eats food, she gets it everywhere
On the table
In her hair
She acts like she lives in a stable.

When she doesn't get her own way
She wrinkles her face
And clutches her dolly,
She's growing at an extreme pace,
I think we're going to call her Molly.

Hannah Reddington (8)
Edlesborough School

THE DEAD OF NIGHT

Do you know what's out at night,
When there isn't a spark or hint of light?
Air thin and icy cold,
Stars twinkling bright and bold.

Black alley cats pouncing and prowling,
Barking hounds chasing and howling.
The moon is bright and keeps shining on,
The stars keep twinkling till the night's gone.

So now you know what's out at the dead of night,
Till the first spark or hint of light.

Rosanna Rice (11)
Edlesborough School

THE THIEF

I'm a thief,
I like to creep around the house,
Looking for food,
People in the living room don't know I'm here.
Up in the bedroom,
I'm looking for food,
I will check the bin,
But there's nothing there
And check under the bed,
I see something red,
It's a . . .
It's an apple,
It's juicy and red,
It lies under the bed,
I hear someone coming.

Aaahhh!
Mum why is there a badger in my room?

Charlie Dear (10)
Edlesborough School

THE LITTLE RAINDROP

I'm a little raindrop in a cloud
I can see all around,
I go down in a puddle and I
Start to paddle.
When I finished paddling,
I started to travel.

Abigail Louise Pearce (9)
Edlesborough School

WHY?

Why are colours so bright?
Why do we have night?

Why are planets all around?
Why do we stand on the ground?

Why are chicks alive?
Why don't hens dive?

Why do dogs bark?
And why do we go to the park?

Why do people wait?
And why do we paint?

Why do people lie?
And why do we die?

Just why?

Emily Lake (8)
Edlesborough School

THE BADGER

My bedroom is dark and scary
A badger is under my bed,
It's black and white and has a bite
It comes out at night, it gives
Me a big, big fright, it can see
But not at night.

Alex Kirkwood (10)
Edlesborough School

WATER PARTICLES

I'm in a cloud waiting to fall
Crash, bang, this is my call
Here I go, falling down
Splish, splash, I hit the ground.

Into the river, moving fast
Friends and fishes swimming past
Around the corner to the sea
Faster and faster I am free.

The water is slowing down
Turning to a muddy brown
Through the filter, getting clean
What does all this mean?

Through the tap into the sink
The speed is starting to make me blink
Down the plug, swirling around
With a loud gurgling sound.

Into the sewers, filtered through
Time to go back up to the queue.

Alex Lay (9)
Edlesborough School

HIDDEN TREASURE

My garden that nobody knows
It's a secret garden at night it goes
It hides away out of sight
It cannot be seen when there is no light.

In the morning my garden appears
If it hadn't I'd have been full of tears
I play in my garden all day long
With so many toys I can't go wrong.

My garden is like a treasure chest
With loads of games that are the best
It's for me and my best friends
But not the rest.

At the end of the day when the sun goes down
It disappears without a sound
I hope it comes back another day
So that me and my friends can play.

Chris Cutler (10)
Edlesborough School

POEM

Under my bed was a white and black badger
sleeping like a baby,
It carefully closed its eyes,
dreaming about flies.
Up I came, looking for yum
to fill my tum.
I see nice worms, yum, yum
in my tum.
Flip, flop, my belly dropped
I'm stuffed up.
I like to be white and black
creeping to the midnight snack.
Jumping belly as I go, no one knows
what I do or what I see, but that's just me.
I creep through noise
I jumble the toys,
creeping back to the midnight snack.
In I go in my deep black, dark hole.

Charlotte O'Sullivan (9)
Edlesborough School

THE THIEF

It creeps around the
Room at night,
It's slick and quick,
It doesn't miss a trick.
The thing creeps around
Sliding on the ground,
It knows it could be found.
Nobody knows what it is,
They say if they found it
They would smash it in the ground.
He hides in secret under
The bed,
Never comes out unless
It's fed.
He lies in secret so
That they don't know
That there is a badger in
The house,
It scavenges in
Your sock,
Creeps around the bed,
But then decides
To nibble at you instead!
He crawls inside
The toys,
Rolls round and
Round and round,
He jumps up in
The air,
Then falls back
To the ground!

Edward Poole (9)
Edlesborough School

TREASURE, TREASURE

Treasure, treasure.
Oh how I wish I could have treasure!
Gold so pure, it's like a dream.

Treasure, treasure, I love treasure
I want a year's supply
Silver up to my eyes.

Treasure, treasure, I need every speck in the world
I want all of it
Gold and silver, up to the sky.

Treasure, treasure, all will be mine
I want it, I'll have it
Gold and silver, no bronze.

Wow! Treasure, treasure, I've found it
It looks like it's worth tonnes,
It's gold so pure, it's like a dream.

Wow! Treasure, treasure, I have it
It's a years supply
Silver all the way up to my eyes.

Wow! Treasure, treasure it's mine
I wanted it, I've got it
It's gold, the most

Wow! Treasure, treasure, it's mine
I'm not sharing it.

Danielle Rutter (10)
Edlesborough School

THE BADGER

Rustling of the trees at night,
Wakens the animal, which gives you a fright.
Digging deep down under the ground,
This greedy animal, scavenges around.
Eating all the food he can find.
Ready to sleep and eat and whine,
Eating worms and meat and mice,
Which to him, would taste very nice.
Scary and frightening, out in the dark,
Sleeping peacefully, when up comes the lark.
Staying in his den all day,
But getting up when it starts to get grey.
When this animal comes out at night,
I promise you he will give you a fright.
He has big teeth and scary paws,
Which will chew and bite and scratch at doors.
The animal I am describing is a *badger!*

Emily Thorne (9)
Edlesborough School

THE FOREST

I walk through the forest with my dog,
I fumbled and tripped in the fog.
The swaying trees block out the sun,
My dog smelled something fishy and he started to run,
He found a dead mole, with luck
But up behind us came a noise.

We left, but it was getting hot and I hadn't got my cap,
So I stopped and took a quick nap.
When I woke, I leapt up high
When suddenly a little fly came buzzing by.

The leaves swept in my face,
As my dog and I had a running race.
The wind was strong, so I hid,
But my dog started to run and I slid.
What would we do without the forest?

Samantha Mead (9)
Edlesborough School

THE CITY OF RISTY

Zero G and Chaz 2 found a hidden path
On the way they found the sea.
They looked for a raft
But there was a sudden draft
Which pushed them in.
They saw a ship in the sea
They went inside
Before there was suicide.
They looked around
But something was out of bound
It looked kind of round
They saw then the city
But it was a pity
There was a floating kitty.
They needed a crane
But they got a train
They got it up
Then there was an interruption.
They went back up the path
Then they saw . . .
A giraffe
In the bath!

Ben Turner (9)
Edlesborough School

FRISKY AND THE CLOUD

There once was a tree called Frisky
Who had a good friend in the sky,
This good friend was a cloud
Who was leader of all clouds nearby.

One day there was a rush of wind
Which blew rubbish into the scene,
Aluminium cans and old rubber tyres
Where the green grass had been.

He yelled up to his friend the cloud
'I need some help down here,
This rubbish tip has got to go -
Your friends could make it clear.

Tell the sun to shine, cloud,
Tell the wind to blow,
Melt the rubber till it's gone
And clear the air below.

Let ice and snow drop on it, cloud,
Let rain chase it away,
Wash the earth with water, cloud
And make it a bright new day.'

Jessica Evans (9)
Edlesborough School

MATERIALS POEM

Rubber is bendy and stretchy
Like an elastic band.

Ice is cold and slippery
You just can't get it in your hands!

Paper is white and smooth,
Sometimes it can leave you bleeding!

Air is invisible and it helps your breathing,
It spreads around, even to the ceiling!

Water is heavy and gleaming,
When you're covered with it, it's hard to move!

Aluminium is shiny and smooth,
It really gets you in the groove!

Martin Coates (9)
Edlesborough School

EXPLORER

There I was standing at the front of the ship
Sailing for the great icy continent of Antarctica
Then I saw it, the great lumbering pack of ice
Coming towards us
Crack went the ice as it splintered on the bow of the ship

Then in front of me loomed the mountain of Erebus
'Land ahoy,' shouted all of the men as they jumped up in joy
Suddenly there was a jerk as we smashed into land
Get all the gear off and we will set off tomorrow.

Five days out, a grimacing and blisteringly cold blizzard blew up
We walked on, but still the storm raged until we had to make camp
Endless walking and camping through the icy white wilderness
Till finally once more we saw the outline of the shore.

The next day we walked up to the shore through the ice-cold wind
There our ship was smashing through the ice towards us
When the ship got to the shore there was a massive
'Hooray'
As we sailed home I thought I was the greatest man alive.

Owain Prys-Jones (11)
Edlesborough School

HIDDEN TREASURE

In the jungle
I had a stumble
Over a snake
Who lived in a lake.
I was very brave
Because I went in a cave.
I saw a pelican
Sitting on a skeleton.
I got stuck in a tomb
Which went boom.
I saw a spider
Flying a glider
With a bottle of cider.
A man said 'Take this treasure!'
So I said 'My pleasure!'

Dean Clark (11)
Edlesborough School

HIDDEN TREASURE

As I ponder down the gravel path surrounded by dew,
I see a door covered in ivy.
I nudge it open,
Inside is another world.
It is not winter but summer,
Flowers scattered everywhere I look.
The scent is astonishing,
The sight is even better.
I walk over the damp grass to a wooden swing
And climb onto it.
This place is magical, I think,
This is my hidden treasure.

Alexander Wade (11)
Edlesborough School

THE NOCTURNAL SCAVENGER

The wet-nosed creature
Creeps slowly through the bright coloured toys
And it makes a lot of noise
I know where it's heading
It's heading for the door
It loves to explore
My pile of toys that's on my bed
The wet-nosed creature
Silently crawls around in the night
It viciously crawls its way through my mattress
Into its fluffy den
It loves to explore my bin
For something to eat
It hibernates in the winter
And it is lively in the summer.

Yep, you guessed it, it's a badger!

Tamzin Holmes (9)
Edlesborough School

MATERIALS

Rubber is bouncy like a bunny
Paper makes shapes that are funny.
Aluminium foil to wrap up my lunch
Freezing cold ice that's hard to munch
Nice cold water to quench my thirst,
Air for my balloon before it bursts!

Kealie Barrett (9)
Edlesborough School

FLOWING

The water flows like a bird, gliding downstream,
leaping over rocks to avoid their stony surface,
suddenly moving faster as though running away from
the reaching branches of the willows nearby,
getting louder, faster, bubbling up like fizzy pop,
gushing onward, slowly reaching the edge of the deep.
Scared of where its flowing, then dropping so suddenly,
falling, falling like a wall of silver,
then crashing deep into the river below.
It carries on its journey like a traveller
lost in the fog, puzzled over which path to take,
but yet it still flows onwards through the forest,
The trees twisted and old, but finally the water flows
into the lake to explore its new home.

Lucy Cox (11)
Edlesborough School

HIDDEN TREASURE

I was in the ship looking through the glass
All I could see was nuts and grass.
We had just left the bay
And were now on our way
To see what they say.
We were nearly there
When we got a scare.
We had hit a rock
It was as big as a wooden block
After that we were at the place
And we couldn't see a single case
Then we all had a beer
It doesn't look like there's any treasure here.

Sam Scott (10)
Edlesborough School

THE WHISTLING KETTLE

I was picked up off the shelf,
On a Saturday afternoon,
I was slung in the trolley,
With the rest of the items,
'Bleep, bleep' as I went through the checkout,
I trundled along in the boot of the car,
My box was opened on the kitchen table,
I was carried off towards the tap,
My lid came off and the cold water tumbled in,
I was slammed on the cooker top,
The dial was turned up
And it began to get warm
And warmer . . . and warmer . . . and warmer . . .
Until I blew my . . . *whistle.*
Ooooohhhhhhh.

Chloe Spratt (10)
Edlesborough School

A CORAL REEF

A coral reef; a whole other world,
Glistening, shining, sparkling.
Fish swim by, not noticing its beauty,
But I gaze in wonder.
The rocks glitter like diamonds in the sun,
The plants and creatures come in every shape and size
And probably every colour too.
There must be treasures hidden everywhere around,
There must be something valuable down there.
So when I look at a majestic coral reef,
I dream of gold; of silver and diamonds
And all other riches that must be hidden down there.

Caroline King (11)
Edlesborough School

THE TROUBLE WITH MY CLASS

Right class be quiet while I'm talking.
Class I'm talking.
Be quiet.
Be quiet!
Right class.
Can any of you tell me what's happening today?
David, however much I wish you weren't,
You're in my class so when I say class it applies to you as well.
Can you tell me what's happening today?
I thought not.
I'll give you a clue.
It's exciting.
No Sharon I'm not retiring.
No, the school's not being blown up either.
Shall I tell you?
We're going to the zoo.
Don't groan Roger.
It's your fault we're not going to the fireworks factory.
Do you know why?
Yes.
At the egg farm you pressed a red button
And every single egg went off.
Now let's get into partners and go.
Where's your lunch Natasha?
Paul get off the table.
Sally you can have either Cathy or Janet as your partner
Not both.
Molly do you have to brush your hair non-stop.
Okay Sharon you're right.
Why?
What do you mean why?
You're right because I'm retiring.

Ellen Davies (10)
Edlesborough School

THE RAINFOREST

The rainforest is a magnificent place,
With a canopy like an umbrella,
The sun peeking through the tiny gaps,
Shining onto the floor.

The huge trees tower above everything,
With monkeys leaping from them,
A python curled around one of its great branches,
Watching a sloth dawdle along a branch.

Brightly coloured fish darted down a stream,
As a snake glides through the water,
A low mist just above it
And a strange lizard running on the water.

A snake slithered through the undergrowth
And ants as big as beetles scurried,
A minute, shiny, blue frog sat on pebbles,
While his friends hopped around.

A warthog was drinking from a pool,
But he was in grave danger,
A leopard was stalking him,
Watching him like a hawk.

The leopard moved closer and closer,
Making no sound at all,
He was ready to pounce,
But the warthog spotted him and fled.

Christopher Moseley (11)
Edlesborough School

THE HIDDEN TREASURE

I walk along the dusty tomb floor
My footsteps echo loudly.
My back tingles
I feel something is watching
Bracken cracks beneath my feet.

I feel a spider crawling up my leg
I bend down to get it off
It isn't there!
I feel spooked out
I freeze to the spot.

I see it at last
The hidden treasure
There it is - light.

Stephanie Houghton (10)
Edlesborough School

I WONDER

I wonder if the Queen ever snores in her sleep?
I wonder if she ever gets angry with her servants?
I wonder if her palace has chandeliers and pictures
Of other kings and queens from the past?
I wonder if I could ever be a king?
I wonder if any of my friends have met the Queen?
I wonder if her children get angry with her?
I wonder if people have been rude to the Queen?
I wonder how many houses she owns,
I wonder how many people visit her?
I wonder how much money she has?
I wonder what her job is?
I wonder if I could ever meet the Queen, face to face?

Jonathan Hill (9)
Overstone Combined School

Midnight Creatures

In the night the owl is singing its midnight song
all night long.

The hedgehog is hurrying, scurrying and burrowing
to find its home.

The fox is a thief, who watches the leaves,
who looks for his tea in the bins
blown over by the wind.

As the morning is breaking,
the sun is rising
and people are waking.

Animals creep home to their beds
now it's their turn to sleep.

Ben Latimer (8)
Overstone Combined School

The Weather

Rain, rain I hate its horrible sound
Rain, rain, rain I hate it when it's pouring down.
Rain, rain I hate it when it saturates me.
I hate the sound when the Wellie boot hits the puddle.
Rain, rain, rain I hate the horrible stuff!

Sun, sun I love its shiny rays,
Sun, sun I love the way it keeps you warm,
I love it when there are clear skies,
Sun, sun I love the bright colours it makes.
Sun, sun I love the hot weather it gives you.
Sun, sun I love the stuff!

Sam West (9)
Overstone Combined School

IN MY DREAM I MET THE QUEEN
AT BUCKINGHAM PALACE

In my dream I met the Queen at Buckingham Palace.
I entered into a beautiful, big hall with portraits everywhere,
A glittering crystal chandelier hung above my head,
Before my eyes I could see a huge, marble staircase
With a royal red carpet.

In my dream I met the Queen at Buckingham Palace.
Through a door I found myself in a grand throne room,
A gold throne encrusted with diamonds, rubies and emeralds
Stood before me
And upon the ruby-red cushion sat the queen herself,
Her corgis sat obediently at her feet.

In my dream I met the Queen at Buckingham Palace.
She wore a gold crown covered in jewels,
Like a ring of burning fire on her head.
She wore a royal blue silk gown with diamonds as buttons,
She wore high-heeled shoes studded with emeralds.

In my dream I met the Queen at Buckingham Palace.
Out in the gardens I stood on a neatly cut lawn,
Bright flowers all around and vines high above the ground.
Guards marched up and down just around the corner
And by a stable full of horses stood a shiny, clean, white
Limousine.

In my dream I met the Queen at Buckingham Palace.
I saw in the dining room, a table a mile long,
Gold padded, velvet chairs set all along
And a scrumptious roast dinner waiting to be eaten.
When in my dream I met the Queen at Buckingham Palace.

Abigail Fairbairn (11)
Overstone Combined School

THE QUEEN

I look around,
I don't know how I got here, do you?
I feel like I've just stepped into a church,
Shadows loom in the corners like animals
Waiting to pounce.
I creep from room to room,
Some with wallpaper others painted.
I'm in a dream aren't I?

The Queen herself is above me,
I look around and see a dead dove in a painting
Poor little thing.
This corridor goes on forever!
The walls are rich red while this ceiling is
Painted with so much care.
The portraits seem to follow me wherever I go
Whatever I do.
There are vases from the Far East and places like Greece.

But as the morning sun slides above the horizon
Like a fiery ball,
A bird makes a call like a song in the distance.
I walk into the biggest room yet,
With a ceiling as high as the sky!
There is her throne, choked with pillows and fabrics
And yes a few diamonds.

What's happening? The ceiling is disappearing
There's a mist
I open my eyes, it was only a dream,
I told myself it was only a dream.

Harriet Gordon-Head (10)
Overstone Combined School

I WANT TO MEET THE QUEEN

The moment I fall asleep, the dream I always dream,
The wish I wish on my birthday cake
And I'm there in the count of three.
The shiny, crystal chandelier hung up on the ceiling high,
The carpet in the corridor, red, springy and fine.

Portraits hung upon the wall, of people long ago.
Some happy, some sad and some you just don't know!
With diamonds, rubies and emeralds patterned round large mirrors.
But then I stop . . . a room that caught my eye!

So I slowly walk into it and stop and stare.
I see the queen for the very first time,
What a shock!
I am really happy and excited!
The Queen sat down on a golden throne!

The corgis sat round in a circle watching each other
Being brushed and groomed.
With a cushion for every one, satin, silk and smooth
Of the colours red, purple and blue!

The stained glass windows all pretty patterns,
With Jesus and others too!
So grant me this wish please Fairy Godmother
And maybe one day I really will meet the Queen.

Leah Fitzgerald (10)
Overstone Combined School

QUEEN ELIZABETH II

It all happened in a marvellous dream:

I walked down the royal hall of Buckingham Palace,
The walls covered in portraits of the royal family.
The long ceiling painted fresh, pure white, like snow,
Chandeliers covered in golden diamonds,
The windows layered in silky curtains.

I opened a huge pine door,
Inside there were shelves choked with red, china ornaments,
A wooden fire glowing on the shiny wooden floor.
In the corner of the room, there was a small wooden staircase,
I lightly put my trainers on one of the stairs,
It made a small creak.

I started walking up the staircase,
When I got up there I found myself in Queen Elizabeth's bedroom.
The room was huge, more chandeliers were hanging from the ceiling.
In a chair near the window I could see the queen sipping a cup of tea,
I walked closer, the queen's corgis were next to her,
Their fat bellies out on the floor.

The bedroom had a huge bed with pure gold curtain rails,
The covers were covered in crochet patterns,
All of a sudden I woke up, it had all been a dream.

Jessica Axten (11)
Overstone Combined School

I Wonder What Buckingham Palace Looks Like?

I wonder how big the Buckingham Palace really is?
Is it small or is it big?
Is it quiet or is it loud?
Is the Queen really proud?
Oh will someone please tell me what it's like.

Does it have stairs that wind in and out like a snake?
Does it have chandeliers which glitter in the light?
Does it have a swimming pool?
Do the servants have some fights?

Does it have gold four-poster beds,
Where the Queen lays her sleepy head?
I wonder how many servants she has . . . one or more?
Oh will someone please tell me what it's like.

I wonder what the Golden Jubilee is going to be like?
Is it going to be celebrated a lot or not?
Will there be a party, or just an ordinary day?
Will we have to pay?

Danny Wright (11)
Overstone Combined School

Not Last Night But The Night Before

Not last night but the night before,
I heard a little knocking on the door.
I went downstairs to let her in,
She said 'Hello, may I come in?'

'The Queen!' I screamed, 'The Queen is here.'
'Please, please, please don't scream, my dear.
I've come here to ask a great favour,
But you have to be on your best behaviour.'

Can I sleep in your big bed,
To rest my tiny, weary, head?
I love my palace, but it's much too big,
And all my servants keep doing a jig.'

'Yes you can, but do me one favour,
Write your autograph on this piece of paper.
There it's done! Now go to bed
And rest your tiny, weary, head.'

David Jarman (11)
Overstone Combined School

DREAMING ABOUT THE QUEEN

I fish a dream from my mind,
And leave all the others behind,
About the Queen
Who is healthy and clean
With all her glassy things
And her shiny gold rings.

When I knocked on her door,
I fell flat on the floor.
And there was the biggest room
I had ever seen before.
It was packed full of beautiful things,
The huge mirrors, the giant doors,
Just the stairs made my mouth water.

She had famous items on display,
Which meant I would have an interesting day,
The Queen's Jubilee
Is very special to me!

Edward Pugh (10)
Overstone Combined School

I Wonder

I wonder what it's like?
You know! Being the Queen?
Does she have her en suite
In her bedroom?
Or her very own limousine?
Or does she keep an elephant
In her royal garden?
Does she have her own servant
To wash up all the dishes?
Does she have a great big pool?
And a tank full of fishes?
Does she ever have second thoughts
About being the Queen?
I wonder what it's like
You know, being the Queen?
Is Buckingham Palace
As nice as chocolate?
Or just old-fashioned.
I wonder what it's like?

Alexandra Gordon-Stuart (10)
Overstone Combined School

Last Night I Had A Dream . . . I Met The Queen

Last night I had a dream
Not a dream which made me scream
I visited the palace to see the Queen
Now I don't suppose you've ever seen
Such a person as the Queen?

I met the children Anne and Ed
But Charles and Andrew were sent to bed
'Would you like some tea?' the Queen said
The horses and dogs had to be fed
Even though one was dead.

When at last I said goodbye
Back to Earth I had to fly
I sat up in bed with a sigh
And all the time I wondered why!
Why did I have that dream about the Queen?

Edward Fairbairn (8)
Overstone Combined School

I WONDER IF . . .

I wonder if the Queen is polite!
I wonder what her house is like?
Does she like it a lot?
I wonder if her butler's tall?

I wonder if she likes having thirty Godchildren
Will I ever want that many?
I wonder if she'll ever want to meet me?
I wonder if I'll ever meet her?

I wonder if she wants to be the best queen?
I wonder if I'll make a good queen?
I wonder if she likes being a queen,
I wonder if she wonders a lot?

I wonder is she's ever fallen off her chair?
I wonder if she's had any accidents?
I wonder if she wishes she was normal?
I wonder if she likes her job?

I wonder if she liked school?
I wonder if she passed her 'A' levels?
I wonder many things!
I wonder if they'll come true!

Freya Hawkins (10)
Overstone Combined School

PEOPLE, PEOPLE

The snow
is like my
mum covering
me with a warm
blanket, though snow
is as cold as an ice cream.
The hail is as rough and tough
as my brother. The sun is like my
dad, kind and warm and big, but is
sometimes hidden by the clouds.
Wind is like my uncle, strong
but good fun.
Rain is like my cats, the
sounds of the raindrops
sounds like they're
purring.

Jessica Smith (9)
Overstone Combined School

THE ENORMOUS STORM

The enormous storm started when it got really windy,
Whirlwinds started blowing all over the town
Gusts of wind were blowing leaves about
Freezing cold weather freezes your hand
Hurricanes blow down trees on beaches
Cyclones are ripping up the sea
Twisting and turning
Finally, the storm moves on to a different place.

Daniel Rixson (8)
Overstone Combined School

THE WEATHER

When it is a bright sunny day.
God is happy.
When it is a dark cloudy day,
God is stroppy.
When it is a dark stormy day,
God is angry.
When it is a wet rainy day,
God cries.
When it is a cold snowy day,
God is cold.
When it is a windy day,
God is drying his beard with a hairdryer
When it is an earthquake,
God is shaking.
When it is a freezing frosty day,
God is sprinkling sugar on a cake.

Samantha Foot (8)
Overstone Combined School

THE RAIN

The rain drizzles down the windows.
The rain pours down from the sky like arrows,
It splashes on the pavements all around.
The rain trickles down the black gutters.
The rain spits down into the small cracks in the road.
The rain drops down on car windscreens.

Harry Tregartha (8)
Overstone Combined School

A DREAM ABOUT THE PALACE

Late last night, I had a dream
About going to the palace,
Opening those magic doors,
Suddenly . . . silence!

Walking right past the winding stairs,
Looking at all the pictures, spying on us.
The chandeliers glistening up ahead,
The ornaments lying all around.

There was the Queen, there was the Queen!
Sitting on a chair
She smiled at me and disappeared.
I really wish I lived there.

Amy Goss (10)
Overstone Combined School

THE RAIN

The rain is horrible, wet and drizzly
Sometimes it pours, sometimes it spits
But I know when it's about to rain.
Horrible grey and white clouds appear in the sky
At first it drips, then it showers.
After the rain, horrible mud puddles appear but . . .
I do like to splash in them!
Sometimes I see mists when we are in the car
And when it rains we have to use our windscreen wipers.
I don't like rain!
When it's cold and it has rained,
The puddles turn into ice.

Ruby Lewis (8)
Overstone Combined School

QUEEN ELIZABETH

Q uite a remarkable lady
U sually with Prince Philip
E legant
E ach day, another visit
N ever goes anywhere alone.

E verybody wants to meet her
L ovely jewellery
I s very intelligent
Z oom lens cameras take her pictures
A lways the Ambassador
B uckingham Palace is her London home
E xtremely busy
T ime to congratulate her Golden Jubilee
H appy birthday Your Majesty!

Chloe Malin (9)
Overstone Combined School

THE STORM

The black, noisy clouds are rushing across the evil sky,
It is always moving like a herd of bulls in a field.
It is as noisy as a band and its clashing is like cymbals.
Whenever there is a jolt of lightning,
It clashes down to Earth.
The storm is a horrendous house,
It frightens me every time.

Kieran Bunce (9)
Overstone Combined School

HOW LUCKY IS THE QUEEN?

How lucky is the Queen?
Was my dream last night,
Which gave me such a fright.

How lucky is the Queen?
Red carpets, chandeliers,
Was the subject of my dream.

How lucky is the Queen?
Tables, mirrors (only the finest!)
Was the subject of my dream.

How lucky is the Queen?
Money, gardens,
Was the subject of my dream.

How lucky is the Queen?
Presents, jewellery,
Was the subject of my dream.

How lucky is the Queen?
Dresses, services,
Was the subject of my dream.

How lucky is the Queen?
Meetings, presentations,
Was the subject of my dream.

How lucky is the Queen?
All those decisions to make,
Was the subject of my dream.

How unlucky is the Queen?
Jeers and boos,
Was the subject of my dream.

Jake Stanmore (11)
Overstone Combined School

I WONDER

I wonder if the Queen ever cries
If she's ever been deeply upset?
If someone has ever called her names?
No, never!

I wonder if the Queen is ever horrible,
If she has ever hurt anyone's feelings?
If she strops if she doesn't get her way?
No, never!

I wonder if the Queen is greedy
If she demands money?
If she is never satisfied with all her fame and wealth?
No, never!

I wonder if she never listens?
If she listens to no one's plan but her own?
If she dismisses everyone else's ideas
Before she even hears them?
No, never!

I expect the Queen is kind and thoughtful
And always speaks her mind
And thinks of others before herself.
But sometimes she can probably be a bit stroppy,
A bit sad and a bit greedy.
No, never!

Jenni Duncumb (10)
Overstone Combined School

THE DREAM OF THE GRUESOME TREASURE

I found a teddy one day,
I said 'You will stay.'
I could not rest my head
unless I had my precious ted.
The more I tried and tried
the more I cried and cried.
When I went to bed one night
I woke up with a terrible fright,
that Ted had turned into a gruesome thing
with sharp claws that would definitely sting.
A gruesome face that was out of place
an enormous green body with hair
that was mouldy and soggy.
I jumped out of bed frightened
of all these things in my head.
My mum said, 'Don't worry, they were
only dreams because Ted is still in your bed.'

Nathan James (9)
Pirton Hill Junior School

LION

He is very brave
He is very beautiful
He looks good
He is brown and yellow
He is my fellow
He can jump high
He goes to the sky
His name is Simba
He says *'Timberrrrrrrrrrr.'*
He is fast!

Usman Shazad (8)
Pirton Hill Junior School

MY TREASURE ISLAND

My treasure island would be for kids,
No grown-ups allowed,
There'd be arcades
And a maze,
I would have an ice cream parlour,
And you could buy your own car,
You could stay up at night
And play as much as you liked.
Go go-karting
And you could always be laughing,
Free food
You'd never be in a bad mood,
My treasure island,
My treasure island,
What a marvellous place it would be.

Antonio Brownie (10)
Pirton Hill Junior School

SADNESS

I am all alone, no one beside me
No friends around me, no one here to take care of me.
But the dark is here, no light anywhere
I am so sad, with tears falling from my eyes, going down my face.
My feelings are sad, I've got no one to talk to me
People call me horrible names.
Is anyone out there?
I've got nowhere to stay, nowhere to sleep
No one to give me a glass of milk
And no one to say goodnight.

Sophie Neate (8)
Pirton Hill Junior School

NEVER SEEING MY HIDDEN TREASURE

Not having a full family.
Not seeing someone from being young.
Having three when you're supposed to have four.
You need someone to comfort you.
You need someone to fill the hole in your heart.
The hidden treasure I cannot find.

Days pass by, not knowing who or where they can be.
Not a glimpse for years.
Not a thought of happiness can comfort me.
The missing link gone forever.
My dearest dream, gone to waste.

Dear, oh dear, whatever shall I do?
Will I ever one day
Find the real you?

Charis Blake (10)
Pirton Hill Junior School

SADNESS

Sadness is when you get beaten up.
Sadness is when you get lost in the rain.
Sadness is when you are really picked on by bigger people.
Sadness is when my sister jumps on me in the morning and winds me.
Sadness is when Mum shouts at me.
Sadness is things that don't go away.
When big boys are picking on you,
Laughing at you,
Calling you names,
Then loads and loads, really loads of tears drop from your sad face
Like a big, big waterfall.

Jack Penman (7)
Pirton Hill Junior School

MY FANTASTIC VIOLIN

My fantastic violin
It fits neatly under my chin
I'm learning to play
And maybe some day
The sound will be more than a din.

It sits alone in my room
Friday will come around soon
My lesson's at nine
I'll be on time
But the session is over too soon.

Semibreve, minim and quaver
Are the notes I'm learning to savour
If I get them just right
And I practise all night
I hope I can play without waver.

Aisling Maynard (9)
Pirton Hill Junior School

CUDDLY CAT CALLED COBY

Coby runs around like mad,
When he nibbles you, you become very sad,
He's asleep, we're all very glad.

Coby likes to give you a cuddle,
He gets you in a muddle,
Like a piece of puzzle.

I wonder if your cat's like mine?

Richenda Leigh Heyes (10)
Pirton Hill Junior School

THE SCARY NIGHT

I'd been attacked by
a *monster*,
Rarra! Rarra!

I'd been attacked by
a *bee*,
Bzzz! Bzzz!

I'd been attacked by
an *alligator*,
Snap! Snap!

I'd been attacked by
a *snake*
Hiss! Hiss!

I'd been attacked by
a *wasp*,
Sting! Sting!

I'd been attacked by
a *spider*
Creepy! Creepy!

I'd been attacked by
a *'I don't know'*
    You!

Daniel Hill (10)
Pirton Hill Junior School

MY BEST FRIEND

My best friend is very special
She's like a sister to me
We spend all our time together
And that's me and my best friend.

We go dancing,
Boogie boogie is what we do
Me and my best friend enjoy it
And we never break up.

Katie Fairall (9)
Pirton Hill Junior School

THE SUN

The sun looks like . . .
a big bright yellow bowling ball,
a huge bit of pastry,
a pot of glittering gold,
sparkling golden treasure

The sun feels like . . .
a sizzling bowl of soup,
a scalding pan,
an extremely squashed orange,
a burning cheese flan

The sun is . . .
playing tag with clouds,
strong,
a good friend,
a warm glowing feeling

The sun makes us
have a snooze,
have a bright suntan,
sweat badly,
wear sunglasses.

Conor Clarke (9)
Pirton Hill Junior School

MEMORIES OF YOU AND ME

When I was born, you held me tight,
Comforted me when I cried at night.
Always there to give a smile,
Ready to laugh and play all the while.
Pretending to do magic and things like that,
Magicking chocolates out of your hat.
We grew together as the years went by,
I felt like I could touch the sky.
The day came when you had to go,
Since then the time has passed so slow.

I know one day we will meet again.

My grandad,
My one true friend.

Danielle Benson (9)
Pirton Hill Junior School

MY FIRST TOY I PLAYED WITH

My first toy was a dog
his eyes were big and blue
but when I went to touch him
he gave a jig so we went up to the room.
But my dog took something and made it go boom
so we went back down the stairs
and when I wasn't looking my toy dog was eating pears.
So we went outside
but when I wasn't looking he was having a ride.
When I realised my toy dog was dead
I never played with my toy dog again.

Joanne Brown (9)
Pirton Hill Junior School

THE SKY

The sky looks like . . .
Fluffy, floating sheep grazing in the sky,
Snow floating firmly through the others,
Big blobs of screwed-up paper,
A gentle blue fleece flying over us,
The blue, blue sea above us.

The sky is . . .
Blue eyes looking down on us,
Blue, blue blankets covering us,
It brings down certain air, cooling us down.

The sky makes us . . .
Feel really calm,
Feel like there are different shapes in the sky.

Shane Sutton (8)
Pirton Hill Junior School

I'VE GOT THE PS ONE

I've got the PS One,
Wish I could win in the place No.1,
And sometimes it even goes ping
Then here comes a bee, arrgh, sting!

I've got the PS One,
That is so special,
With Tony on it, it makes his leg numb
And I would sell it for a £100 or more for all,
My PS One is so great,
That some people even hate,
Mine can even walk and talk.

Oliver Meaton (10)
Pirton Hill Junior School

A Pirate Out At Sea

A t the beginning,

P eople feared pirates,
I n fact they hated them,
R eally they weren't that bad,
A fter you got to know them,
T hey just wanted their treasure,
E ven though they killed.

O ut at sea,
U could see,
T he ships out at sail.

A ll aboard the ship,
T he crew would shout,

S ailing around the world,
E vening, noon and night,
A fter all the treasure.

Simon Catton (9)
Pirton Hill Junior School

My Hidden Treasure

The sea is blue
The boat rocks too.
Deep under the sea
the treasure is free.
People try to grab it but
they just can't have it.
You see
it belongs to me.
My hidden treasure.

Jodi Roach (9)
Pirton Hill Junior School

SCHOOL

No more biology,
No more technology,
No more French,
Why did they take down the old school bench?

No more literacy,
No more maths,
No more science,
When it's naff!

No more spellings,
No more tests,
No more SATs and
Give us a rest!

Rest is pleasure,
Just like treasure!

Stephen Avery (9)
Pirton Hill Junior School

THE STONE

I'm looking for a stone,
That looks like a bone.

I'm looking everywhere,
I think it might be over there.

I'm staying on my feet,
And I'm dancing to the beat.

I found it right there,
And it's lying on a stair!

I've found it!

James Kissane (9)
Pirton Hill Junior School

FIREWORKS

On Bonfire Night I go to see fireworks,
I see them gleaming in the sky,
They sparkle and glitter over my head,
Goodbye, goodbye, goodbye,
Now they start spreading,
Big and small, bright and colourful,
Banging as loud as they can,
It gives me pleasure once a year,
To come and watch the fireworks appear,

It's finally time to say goodbye

Bang!

We'll meet again on Bonfire Night.

Tanisha Darji (10)
Pirton Hill Junior School

PIRATES

Pirates were thought to be gone,
But one night the pirates were back,
To attack a small town called Dover City,
The thieves were going to nick one thousand pounds,
The people yelled 'Help, help, help!'
As they nicked cakes, money, oil and chips,
The pirates started to shoot some oil barrels,
However the pirates nicked the fastest ship in the world
And put a bomb next to £1,000,000 of oil.
Dover City and the pirate ship were gone.

Nathan Williams (10)
Pirton Hill Junior School

ALL KINDS OF BEARS

There are big, brown and black bears
and even yellow bears like Winnie the Pooh,
but my teacher calls him Winnie the Plop.

Nice bears, nasty bears, cuddly bears,
happy bears, angry bears, furry bears,
fat bears, skinny bears!

Bears have big, bright brown, blue and black eyes
which glow in the moonlight.

Bears with big, sharp claws and big, white teeth,
bears have big noses!

Bears move like my brother when he has just got out of bed.
Bears can stand up like a human when they're drunk,
crazily waving their arms around and roaring and singing.

Chloe Lawrence (11)
Pirton Hill Junior School

MY GREAT NAN

She silently sat peacefully in the comfortable rocking chair,
The blazing fire shimmered in the darkness,
The fire reflected her white hair,
She always used to smile at me with happiness.
Her soft, peach hands touched my face,
My great nan was so kind,
She had lovely clothes made out of lace,
All the memories are left behind.
I love my great nan.

Rebecca Rowley (9)
Pirton Hill Junior School

WHAT RATS DO

My name is Rizzo, the rat,
I live at home with birds and fish,
And also a grey and white cat,
I eat my food out of a dish.

The colour of my fur is brown and white,
My tail and whiskers are long,
Though people are scared, I do not bite,
Even though my teeth are strong.

I look like a squirrel when I eat my food,
I sit down and eat with my paws,
I like to chew on straw and wood,
To sharpen my teeth and claws.

I run up the stairs to keep me fit,
A couple of times a day,
Then next to my tank, Tamara and Georgia sit,
While I sleep the day away.

Tamara Porritt (8)
Pirton Hill Junior School

LIONS

He is big, he picks on
Small animals
He is strong, he picks on
Weak animals.
He scares animals with his growl.
He lives on his own.
He has a big scar on his side
Where he was once attacked.

Louis Devall (8)
Pirton Hill Junior School

MY FRIEND

A charming creature,
an elegant brown cat,
a brown, glittering star.

She feels like . .
a flower tickling me,
a warm hand touching me,
velvet petals.

My friend . . .
is an enjoyable person,
a brainbox,
an amusing clown.

My friend looks like . . .
a pitch-black cat,
the appearance of her and her delightful sight,
her pretty, brown, glistening hair.

Leanna Atkinson (9)
Pirton Hill Junior School

CATS

My cat Tom is a pain in the backside
He is always outside wanting his dinner
Here I am doing his dinner
He is purring outside
Running up and down the decking.

Fed and lazy now
He lies on my bed all day
I cuddle him
And he cuddles me.

Chelsea Smith (8)
Pirton Hill Junior School

BUSTER

Buster Baxter Boxer Dog,

Found him in a rubbish box.
Took him home to fuss and love
Buster Baxter Boxer Dog.

When we got home,
'I want a bone,' he said
And chocolate buttons on my toes.
Buster Baxter Boxer Dog.

When he was three
He weed up a tree!
Buster Baxter Boxer Dog.

When he was four,
He could open the door.
Buster Baxter Boxer Dog.

When he was five,
He learnt to drive,
Buster Baxter Boxer Dog.

Nicole Baxter (8)
Pirton Hill Junior School

THE SNAKE IN THE LAKE

What I hate about a snake is it slithers.

What I like about a snake is it's colourful.

What I hate about a snake is its tongue darts in and out
And it eats nasty things like rats and frogs.

What I like about a snake is how it curls.

Andrew Day (8)
Pirton Hill Junior School

THE WIND

I can be as strong as an iron block
Or as weak as a flower!

I can blow down skyscrapers
Or blow whole towns, villages and cities into submission!

I can be as quiet as a mouse
Or as loud as an elephant!

For I am the wind! Yes, the wind!
Of course, did you think I was a giant vacuum?

I can creep up on you in the form of mist
Or suck you up as a giant tornado!

Destroy or wreck your town as a powerful hurricane windstorm!

Wind, yes, wind, for if you please
I am not all bad! Watch!

I can block out the sun if it's too bright!

I can remove myself if it's too dark!

Ross Moseley (10)
Pirton Hill Junior School

REBECCA

R   is for robins that fly
E   is for eating Christmas pudding
B   is for betting in a game
E   is for eggs, yummy and scrumptious
C   is for Christmas dinner
C   is for quiet in the classroom
A   is for apple to eat.

Rebecca Mynard (9)
Pirton Hill Junior School

SUMMER

The sun . . .
The sun is as beautiful as a glistening orange,
a sparkling sun in the glistening sky,
the sun looks at everybody playing on the beach.

People playing . . .
in the garden on a summer's day,
outside their houses in the blue glamorous sky.

The beach . . .
people going to the seaside in the appearing blue sky,
elegant young children making sandcastles, charming and brown,
the beach in the summer is pleasant and affectionate.

Feels like . . .
a person being tickled on the back,
I love the beach because it's lovely and hot for me,
I feel overjoyed when I am at the beach.

Nicola King (8)
Pirton Hill Junior School

WHEN I'M OLDER

When I'm older
What does that mean?
What? What? What?
Maybe I'll be a judge and study the law
Or a farmer and sell fruit and veg.
Maybe I'll be a psychologist or even a scientist.
Or a doctor or a nurse.
Maybe I should think this over
          and come back to you when I'm older.

Gladys Mugugu (10)
Pirton Hill Junior School

THUNDER AND LIGHTNING

A thunderstorm can be scary . . .
While lightning can be extremely flarey
Oh no, the poor farmer's dairy
With a bash and a smash it's fallen down.

A thunderstorm can be . . .

Swwww!
B b bang!
Pitter-patter, pitter-patter,
It's also a big, grey ball of cotton wool,
Was the lightning frightening enough?
There goes the farmer's straw,
1, 2, 3, 4, hooray, it's over and gone to Dover.

Charlene Warner (9)
Pirton Hill Junior School

WHAT IF?

What if the world was square and the moon was orange
And Henry VIII was really Rolf Harris?
What if people could fly and birds could swim
And my dad could calm down a bit?
What if Doctor Who could tell us his name
And the Daleks could actually exterminate people?
What if the world stopped spinning
And Germany could beat England in football?
What if a dictionary said 'I'm a jerk' on the front
And a thesaurus sang 'Baa, baa black sheep' when opened?
Wouldn't it be a wonderful world
If I ever *shut up!*

Paul Stiff (11)
Pirton Hill Junior School

TWO BAD CATS

Two bad cats
Sitting on their mats
Wearing bowler hats
Looking for rats
Oh! What bad pussy cats
Chasing mice
Mice are nice
Would you like a slice
With some rice
That would be nice
I could eat it twice
Grinned the naughty pussy cats
Oh what bad pussy cats!

Hayley Russell (8)
Pirton Hill Junior School

MY SPEED

I am one with the night,
Stealing through the mist
Like a jungle cat.
I am dashing through the field,
Soaring across the grass
As it whips my heels.
Miles and miles I travel,
Now I'm hovering over the soft, sandy mud,
As it clutches at my feet.
I rapidly cross the rickety bridge,
Then my feet pound on the snow,
As I cross the weary mountainside.

Samuel Hogarth (11)
Pirton Hill Junior School

THE STARS

The stars look like . . .
a small piece of cut paper,
a white fluffy cat up a tree,
a flower blooming in the sky

The stars feel like . . .
a piece of paper crunching
a spongy ball of water

The stars are . . .
like a sunlight up in the sky,
like a light

The stars make us . . .
gaze into the sky,
go to bed
and think of things.

Benisha Janse van Rensburg (9)
Pirton Hill Junior School

LITTLE TOM THUMB

There once was a boy called Tom Thumb.
He had lots of friends and a chum.
He was very small, you couldn't really see him at all.
Because he was very small.
He got stuck to the wall.
He had scruffy boots, he was picking out some roots,
He couldn't go to school, no way!
He would get squashed every day.
He had short hair, a bit was curved,
'Children should be seen and not heard!'

Bradley Yates (8)
Pirton Hill Junior School

SUMMER

Summer looks like . . .
a bright blue sky,
sunflowers growing to the highest height,
buzzing bees collecting pollen,
flowers popping out of the ground.

Summer feels like . . .
a warm breeze in the air,
the sun shining happily,
a very hot season.

Summer makes me . . .
go on holiday,
plant flowers,
very happy,
wear summer clothes and hats.

Summer is . . .
the sun's holiday,
a sunny season,
a joyful season,
an enjoyable time.

Megan Graham (9)
Pirton Hill Junior School

ACCIDENT!

What if I kicked my PlayStation?
Ouch, my foot!
Imagine the PlayStation rocketing off the wall.
What if I got rushed to A & E
And I kept on screaming, 'My knee!'?
I would kick the man carrying the tea.

Anthony Cutler (11)
Pirton Hill Junior School

A PUPPY

Runs like . . .
A speedy rocket from outer space,
A person blinking very rapidly,
A shooting star in the black night sky.

Feels like . . .
A furry, fluffy teddy in my bed,
Cotton wool in a ball,
A cosy cover with a puffy pillow.

Barks like . . .
A massive banging band of drums,
A big balloon popping loudly,
A person sadly screaming.

Looks like . . .
A funny, skinny little costume,
As tiny as a squeaking mouse,
A fiercely furry lion.

Chelsea Mason (8)
Pirton Hill Junior School

TOYS

Toys are good
Toys are great
All the boys
Show them to their mates
Girls are buying Barbie dolls
Boys are scoring lots of goals.

Jake Green (8)
Pirton Hill Junior School

SNOW

Snow looks . . .
As white as a clean sheet of paper,
Something funny and crunchy that you can play with all day,
Something smooth and flat waiting there to be stepped on,
Like a tiny, fluffy ball.

Snow feels . . .
As thin and as soft as a piece of hair,
As rough as sandpaper,
As cold as a cube of ice,
As much fun as an amazing firework.

Snow makes us . . .
Delighted and cheerful,
Think of a beautiful, white Christmas,
Go out and play snowball fights,
Catch a terrible cold that we hate.

Snow is . . .
Sparkling in the freezing cold,
Having fun with children,
Lying on the ground waiting patiently,
Up in the sky sitting there for the right time to come down.

Adelaide Hetherington (8)
Pirton Hill Junior School

TIGER

This cat is big,
He has stripes,
Good at getting his prey,
Ears are good at hearing,
Running fast to get his dinner.

Lewis Hammond (8)
Pirton Hill Junior School

SUMMER

Summer feels like . . .
turning on a light that grows hot and warm
a summer breeze going through your hair,
imagining you're riding a horse in the open
                         fields and then you're there.

Summer looks like . . .
something that you've always wanted
and your favourite place.

Summer makes us . . .
go out in the swimming pool,
go out and have fun,
go to the seaside and
sunbathe under the sun.

Summer smells like . . .
hot dogs, burgers,
Coca-Cola, coffee or tea
the best part about it is
it's all just for me.

Jae Symone Cain-Greaves (9)
Pirton Hill Junior School

MY PET HAMSTER

My pet hamster Speedy Boyle,
Thinks she's rather royal.
Sitting on her royal throne,
She lies down with a moan and a groan
Down upon her featherbed
Big, fat belly, sleepyhead.

Loren Boyle (8)
Pirton Hill Junior School

WANTED TREASURE

I found treasure in the garden,
Should I open it?
Should I open it?
I found treasure in the garden.

So I opened it,
And I had money,
Jewellery and so many to name.

And the next thing I knew,
Someone was knocking on the door,
Saying 'That's my treasure.'
'Go away,' I said.

And a clown was knocking on the door
And then the zoo animals were knocking on the door
And I said, 'I don't have any treasure.'

Nicola Griffiths (9)
Pirton Hill Junior School

ALPHABET POEM

A   is for Abbey who stinks
B   is for Benjamin who always blinks
C   is for Corey who always burps
D   is for Debbie who never works
E   is for Emma who says 'Whatever'
F   is for Fiona who says 'Never'
G   is for Gilbert who is a filler
H   is for Hilda who is a killer
I   is for Ingei whose teeth are fake
J   is for Jack who likes cake.

Kirsty Jade Bradbery (8)
Pirton Hill Junior School

THE RAIN

Rain feels like . . .
having a chilly shower,
freezing one pound coins falling onto your body,
a cold hand touching you over and over again.

Rain looks like . . .
somebody's miserable tears,
snow tumbling out of the air,
silver hailstones falling through the sky.

Rain sounds like . . .
a gigantic giant crying high above the sky,
an enormous pot of gold dripping onto our windows,
pitter-patter dropping on the ground.

Rain makes us . . .
go inside and have nothing to do,
have wet play at school,
wear good waterproof clothes and shoes.

Rebecca Kent (8)
Pirton Hill Junior School

THE SEA

The waves feel like a paintbrush painting over us,
The waves look like a sea monster trying to get the sand.

On stormy nights . . .

The ocean crashes on to the rocks,
and makes huge waves.

On sunny days . . .
The sea drifts from side to side.
It laps quietly and calmly.

Latifah Cain-Greaves (9)
Pirton Hill Junior School

THE SNOW

The snow is
A ball we can throw and play with.
A giant piece of ice falling from the sky.
A frozen star at night.
A massive snowball.
The snow makes us
Frozen, shivering in the snow.
Look like big, freezing people.
Put on a scarf, gloves and hat.
Sometimes feel happy.
The snow feels like
Cold tickling fingers.
A freezing piece of slush.
A round ball of ice.
Freezing cold water running from the tap.
The snow looks like
A tiny iceberg.
A teeny-weeny soft white puppy.
A white ball of fluff.
A big, fat, flubby teddy.

Ria Murphy (8)
Pirton Hill Junior School

THE SNOW

The snow looks like . . .
a piece of raw snow,
a piece of melted ice,
a piece of chilly white meat.

The snow tastes like . . .
a polar bear,
a piece of cold ice,
a really thick piece of paper.

The snow is . . .
as cold as the North Pole,
as frosty as can be,
as stiff as an ice cube.

Niall McKenna (8)
Pirton Hill Junior School

THE SUN

The sun looks like . . .
a flaming bike tyre in the sky,
a round ball of flames,
a boiling hot globe way up high,
a yellow fruit just waiting to be eaten.

The sun feels like . . .
a burning hot cooking pot,
a hundred peppers in some food,
a huge pumpkin on fire,
a bullet piercing your skin.

The sun is . . .
round like an orange,
a sphere of fire,
hiding behind the clouds when it rains,
burning hot when it's warming the world.

The sun makes us . . .
warm and sleepy,
put on a summer hat,
put on suncream and sunbathe,
turn off heaters and run outside.

Joanne Bailey (9)
Pirton Hill Junior School

RAIN

The rain looks like . . .
Water dripping from the sky,
Darkness through clouds.

The rain feels like . . .
A cup of ice melting on my face,
Pit-pat on my freezing cheeks.

The rain sounds like . . .
Hailstones on a car,
A tap dripping,
A pen banging on a table.

The rain tastes like . . .
Cold water,
Ice cubes.

The rain helps us with . . .
Growing food,
Helps flowers and trees grow.

Alicia Burton (8)
Pirton Hill Junior School

WHAT IF . . .?

What if the sky wasn't blue?
What if there was no, 'I love you'?
What if we all stayed two?
What if these all came true?

What if we all turned pink?
What if we all started to stink?
What if we all wanted a drink?
What if we all stopped to think?

What if we all started to drool?
What if there was no more school?
Wouldn't that be totally cool?
(But you would end up like a fool!)

What if the sky wasn't blue?
What if there was no, 'I love you'?
What if we all stayed two?
What if these all came true?

Bryony Coombs (10)
Pirton Hill Junior School

RAIN

The rain makes us . . .
sick to death,
miserable.
The rain can be . . .
dangerous,
gentle,
calm and
fun.
The raindrops like . . .
pouring,
showering,
talking to you.
Water . . .
pours from a waterfall,
drips from taps,
but when it turns to winter,
water turns to ice,
water is like a disliked friend.

Michael Ward (9)
Pirton Hill Junior School

FIRE

Fire looks like . . .

A lane of people with a bad heart,
Colours running around town,
An oven going out of control,
Red, yellow and orange colours bopping up and down.

Fire feels like . . .

A steak on a plate,
And burnt food,
A hot cup of tea,
You'll get in a mood.

Fire warns you like . . .

Never touch matches
You'll lose your life
It can be scary
It's worse than a knife.

Kieran Todd (9)
Pirton Hill Junior School

HIDDEN TREASURES

In a dull, dusty cave
diggers came to dig
dig, dig, dig to find
treasures that were big.

They were here all night
they were here all day
suddenly they found it in
the month of May.

People came and got very excited
people were happy
people were glad
people also went mad.

Then they came back
the very next day
in the month of May
and were told to go away.

Michael Anderson (11)
Pirton Hill Junior School

A LEAF

A leaf feels so . . .
light, soft and so feeble,
like the early morning creeping,
on the ground, wet and damp.

A leaf smells . . .
so fresh like nature,
in the sunny spring,
and like flowers,
like it was the king.

A leaf looks like . . .
an oval with pointy sides,
it looks so shiny in the morning dew,
and a lovely sight to see.

A leaf is . . .
as wonderful as can be,
a raindrop on a leaf,
as comfortable as a cushion.

Chelsea Cosher (9)
Pirton Hill Junior School

THE CHINESE DRAGON

Once there was a Chinese dragon.
He was good
but the king
wanted to
kill the
dragon.
So the king demanded
'I want to kill that dragon.
Whoever kills him
will get a
thousand pounds'
So everyone
said
'That isn't a bad idea.'
'I will do it,'
shouted someone
and a man came in
'I will do it'
(so horrible)
and he shot the dragon and
they never saw him again.

Sean Boyle (10)
Pirton Hill Junior School

ANGRY LION

Look, a lion in a cage
His hairy face like a flower

He will bite you
Killer jaws
Beautiful but deadly.

Mbaki Banda (8)
Pirton Hill Junior School

Roses Are Red, Violets Are Blue

Roses are red,
Violets are blue,
I'm singing this little song
To you.

Daffodils are yellow,
Daisies are white,
All the flowers in the garden
Are really
Bright.

Roses are red,
Violets are blue,
I have finished singing
This song to you.

Lisa Tott (11)
Pirton Hill Junior School

Marshall The Dog

What I hate about dogs is
They slobber on you when
They have just had a drink of water.

What I like about dogs,
They look after you
And they love you.

What I hate about dogs,
They have got gunge in their eyes
And they wipe it on you!

What I like about dogs,
They're fluffy all over.

Annika Crawford (7)
Pirton Hill Junior School

HIDDEN TREASURES

If I found a magic treasure chest,
And I could imagine anything in it,
I would choose . . .

Lots of chocolate, lots of toys,
A bit of peace but quite a lot of noise.

Every single console, every single game,
Lots of money but not to rearrange.

Loads of cool stuff, loads of gadgets,
Traps for robbers so police don't have to catch it.

I can't think of one more thing,
I'm starting to worry with fear
But just when I've thought of it,
Everything's disappeared.

David Pentecost (10)
Pirton Hill Junior School

WHAT IF I?

What if I bought the biggest chocolate bar in the world?
What if I am the fastest person in the world?
What if I am the Prime Minister?
What if I am the richest person in the world?
What if I am a famous football player?
What if I went on a shopping spree?
What if I declared world peace?
What if I owned a Ferrari?
What if I climbed Mount Everest?

I would be proud.

Callum Riordan (10)
Pirton Hill Junior School

HIDDEN TREASURES

My dad has hidden treasure
I don't think it's much of a pleasure
It's terrifying,
If you see it you'll be crying
and believe me I'm not lying.

This treasure is very smelly,
It will make you really sick to your belly
It's been passed down from the old
So be bold but not too bold.

The treasure is very vicious
It will think you're delicious
It will suck you up
And muck you up

But I told you not to be bold.

Ryan Derby (10)
Pirton Hill Junior School

THE TREASURE HUNT

There's treasure over there
No, over there, why is treasure rare?
I'd better look here, I wish it was easy to find.
Oh I will get so mad, I will lose my mind.
Here, I think I've found the treasure
It's just a tape measure
I've found it, pull out the chest,
It's empty, so much for all the rest!

James Ward (10)
Pirton Hill Junior School

HIDDEN TREASURES

One day I was on my way to find a pyramid
And in that pyramid there was a magic lamp.

One day I found a mummy
The mummy was spooky
Then I ran away from it
Then I landed in a pit.

I started sinking, then I was eaten.
I thought, is it a monster?
I got really worried.

I was in another pyramid
I saw another tunnel
In the tunnel I saw a magic lamp
It was old and dusty, blank!

Kirsty Warren (10)
Pirton Hill Junior School

LONELY

Take time and you will find,
Inside I am good and kind,
I try to please,
But no one sees
I want to shout
Let my feelings out,
My character will bend.

All I want is
a friend!

Amber Clairmonte (10)
Pirton Hill Junior School

HIDDEN TREASURES

The only thing that I've ever wanted
was to see real gold.
Real gold that pirates steal.

If I had gold I would buy
everything in the world
and be really rich.

If I had gold I would meet
all the famous people who
play football and are in films.

I would have diamonds and lots
of jewellery to wear to special places.
And I would keep them in the biggest
treasure chest in the world.

Corey Douglas
Pirton Hill Junior School

FAME!

Fame can be fun,
But not for some.
Fame can be nice,
But you have to pay the price.
Fame can reward you,
To see *your* fortune.

But fame can come,
And fame can go,

But most of all,
I have it *all!*

Siobhan Mupemhi (11)
Pirton Hill Junior School

WEIRD ANIMALS

I went to the weirdest animal park,
and saw . . .
A groovy giraffe
walking down the path,
far-out fish
making a wish
cool cats
wearing hats
dopey dogs
with performing frogs
two big apes
sharing grapes
lions with irons
two big cheetahs
who came to meet us
an iguana threw
a banana
two bats met the cats in hats,
for a game of cricket.
I'm going home now,
I can't stick it anymore!

Stephanie Russell (10)
Pirton Hill Junior School

I'M WRITING A POEM

I'm writing a poem, but what about?
Maybe of things in the dark that jump out.
Maybe of monsters all big 'n' scary
Or maybe of monsters all short 'n' hairy.

I'll write it about aliens all gorky 'n' funny
Blue in colour, with a nose that's runny.
Or maybe bright green, with big teeth that gleam,
Or maybe blood-red, with a very big head.

I'll write it about ghosts, that you can see almost.
Or maybe they smell a bit like burnt toast,
Maybe things move, or go bump in the night
So hide under the duvet and hold Teddy real tight!

Daniel Hynes (10)
Pirton Hill Junior School

THE PETS I WANT

In her wheel she runs around,
And speeds in her ball on the soft, green ground,
My hamster is just not the same,
Cleopatra is her name.

My fish swims like a speeding light,
Darting around with all his might,
He came from a pond, upon a hill,
Of course my fish's name is Phil.

My lizard with her emerald scales,
Tries to bite me, but she fails,
Her favourite food is mice and rats,
My lizard's name is Sister Bats.

My frog is so friendly and jumpy,
A Bactrian camel with his back so humpy,
A rat with kids, that I give a rub,
And a crocodile in my bathtub.

A dog will help me round the house,
A cat would help me with a mouse,
All these animals will bring me pleasure,
I'll keep them like a chest of treasure.

Richard Mason (10)
Pirton Hill Junior School

HIDDEN TREASURES

A group of animals find a ship
They go inside and have a peek

They see something shining,
They go on much further
As they see a diamond ring.

They stop for a second
They hear something go
They look through the door
And the ring goes ping.

They see a pearl necklace
With a big pearly ring
They go through the door
And find the most wonderful thing
They find the missing treasure.

There's a box in the corner
Which is moving about
They open it up and out with a clout,
Jumps a puppy
Who lives with treasure on his ship.

Lian Connolly (10)
Pirton Hill Junior School

THE HORSE

It has a fluffy tail and has small nails
It has legs like a giraffe
It has small babies like a calf
It lets you ride on its back
You can keep it as a pet.

Georgina Guy (10)
Pirton Hill Junior School

TREASURE BOX

Necklace, necklace, necklace.
My first necklace, I found it in the cupboard
in a treasure box upstairs.

Earring, earring, earring.
My first earring, I found it in the cupboard
in a treasure box upstairs.

Ring, ring, ring.
My first ring, I found it in the cupboard
in a treasure box upstairs.

Bracelet, bracelet, bracelet.
My first bracelet, I found it in the cupboard
in a treasure box upstairs.

Anita Titmus (9)
Pirton Hill Junior School

THE DINO DINNER

The dino went
To a dinner

And he grew
Thinner and thinner

He had a race
To outer space

He had a golden eye
He could say goodbye

He had a wonder
About the thunder.

Steven Hamond (8)
Pirton Hill Junior School

FIRE, FIRE

Fire burn bright into the sky,
The colours gleam into the moonlight.
The musky smell of burning wood.

Its flames rise into the sky like big arms,
Its face, a bright, yellowy orange and red.

I can't believe my eyes.
It hurts my eyes.

Renate O'Connor (11)
Pirton Hill Junior School

IF ONLY I COULD . . .

If only I could fly up high and touch the sky,
Or have magic powers and use them for hours,
Or be able to turn invisible which is impossible,
Or make people who have died come back to life,

    If only, if only, if only
                       I could.

Jayna Kirankumar Patel (10)
Pirton Hill Junior School

WHY ARE ELEPHANTS LIKE THAT?

Elephants are as tall as trees
Why are they not as small as bees?

Elephants have really thin hair
Why is it not as thick as a bear's?

Elephants are really fat
Why are they not as thin as a cat?

It is said that elephants never forget
They are just too large to be my pet.

Lauren Berry (11)
Pirton Hill Junior School

COBY CAT

What I hate about cats.
Is that they like sitting on my head,
When I have to go to bed.
What I like about cats,
Is that they are playful and fluffy.
What I hate about cats,
Is they scratch all the time,
And their claws dig right into your skin.
What I like about cats,
Is how they snuggle up in your lap.

Stephanie Heyes (8)
Pirton Hill Junior School

MY IMAGINARY WENDY TORTOISE

Wendy Tortoise is her name
Never jumping, never plays
Strays around on lazy days
Cool tortoise
Hard shell, wiggly toes
Little nose
Very slowly comes and goes.

Maya Greenidge (8)
Pirton Hill Junior School

EMMA THE CAT

Emma is a lazy cat
Tall, black
Lazy cat
All she does is sleep on the mat
And eat and sleep
Eat and sleep

She thinks she can fight all night
She has a good appetite
And eats and sleeps
Eats and sleeps.

Leigh Spary (8)
Pirton Hill Junior School

WHY DO?

Why do penguins always waddle?
Short legs tend to make them hobble.

Why do owls always blink?
Big eyes tend to make them think.

Why do flamingos always stand?
When they fly they have to land.

Matthew Fountain (7)
Pirton Hill Junior School

LIZARDS!

Lizards move at the speed of sound.
They can climb up trees out of danger.
They get to safety away from snakes and predators.
They're camouflaged green, the colour of plants.

Lizards are very scaly.
They are good jumpers like kangaroos.
Their claws are as sharp as knives
And they have quick eyes to keep watch on you.

Daniel Smith (11)
Pirton Hill Junior School

DOLPHIN

A dolphin swims in the water,
He splashes and splashes
And he smiles at people
And then he swims away.

When the dolphin jumps from the water
It looks as though he's playing
He likes to get people wet.

He jumps and jumps and he gets the boat wet,
He likes to play.

James Warren (7)
Pirton Hill Junior School

IN THE GARDEN

In the garden there was a box,
A box that was hidden deep in the soil.
The box was gold with lots of pictures,
In the box was jewellery, diamonds, crystals,
                                    rings and necklaces.
A boy came and found it and opened it up.
And what was inside, made him jump.

Joanna Maynard (9)
Pirton Hill Junior School

CROCODILE IN THE LAKE

What I hate about crocodiles
Is they always look at me and
I think they're going to eat me

What I like about crocodiles
Is looking at their skin

What I hate about crocodiles
is they always look at me and no one else
And I don't like it

What I like about crocodiles
Is how they sleep in water.

Lucy Ross (8)
Pirton Hill Junior School

HIDDEN TREASURES

Sparkling jewellery shining bright,
Shimmering in the shining light,
Glittering rings with diamonds in,
Light up when the sun goes dim.

Expensive antiques, valuable gold,
Silver crowns which could never be sold,
Glamorous earrings that sparkle like glitter,
Valuable bracelets that shimmer.

Treasure from Heaven,
My dreams have come true,
I'll sell them all for one million pounds,
For all my dreams have now been found.

Melissa Hudson (10)
Pirton Hill Junior School

HIDDEN TREASURES

Maps, sequins, secrets and dreams
All are as precious and more than they seem.
All of the treasures, bright and antique
While a girl full of treasures whose name is Monique.

Monique is a girl who's from Egyptian times
Who has loads of diamonds which look like mines.
Expensive treasures hidden under the sea
While sea sailors find more than me.

Loads of treasures just sitting there
While they can be found places *elsewhere!*
I have found the treasure all by myself
So it is mine and belongs to
                                        nobody else!

Valerie Tella (10)
Pirton Hill Junior School

MONSTER DAVE

Monster Dave is very naughty
Even though he is forty
All he thinks about is food
But he is still rude
He looks fluffy but
Nothing like his mummy.

Monster Dave has got two kids
He still eats out of bin lids.

When he was small
He liked football.

Shaquille Kandekore (8)
Pirton Hill Junior School

HIDDEN TREASURE

This starts at an island
where I try to find some fabulous gold.
Shiny diamonds and fantastic islands
where people will never go.
Treasure maps and measure maps
will always come in handy,
so let's get digging for old man Higgins
and try to get some glorious gold.

Nicole Bunce (11)
Pirton Hill Junior School

THE ROBIN

A robin has a small nest in a tree.
A robin has some small eggs.
A robin has a red chest.
A bright, bright red chest
And when the sun shines on its red chest
It glows like *fire*
And it shares its brightness with everyone.

Amanda Ayling (10)
Pirton Hill Junior School

THE FURRY, FLUFFY, FLOPPY DOG

What I hate about dogs is
You have to clean up their mess

What I like about dogs is they're furry
And floppy and funny.

What I hate about dogs is
They scare me and chase me home.

What I like about dogs is they wag their tails
And in the night they make you warm in your bed.

Natasha Taylor (7)
Pirton Hill Junior School

BEARS

Bear!
Big and furry
I'm surprised it could get scary
Bear!
Fat and out of shape
Eats loads of meals and fruit like a grape
Bear!
Bear, big and cuddly.

Niran Vaughan (10)
Pirton Hill Junior School

DOGS

Dogs are soft, cuddly and fast.
When they run, their tail wags in the air
As if there is a fly in the air.

When they're hungry, they whimper and cry.
But I love it when they give me a five.

They're playful and fun and like running along.
They're as big as you when they come to see you.

Nathan Batchelor (10)
Pirton Hill Junior School

HIDDEN TREASURES

Five pirates went sailing out to sea
Wondering what to have for tea
They caught some fishes
But they had no dishes
So they had nothing for tea.

They found loads of diamonds
And millions of islands
And found a map on the floor
Saying 'I'm not so poor.'

They looked for the treasure
But not with much pleasure
Then they finally found the treasure.

John McIntyre (10)
Pirton Hill Junior School

MY HIDDEN TREASURE

In the Amazon in Brazil
In the darkest, smelliest, dangerous part of the Amazon,
Is a gigantic tomb, golden brown,
Inside, cobwebs the size of nets,
With a musty smell.
Deadly traps that Indiana Jones wouldn't survive.
If you get past all that
A pit opens beneath your feet,
Before you know it,
You have fallen into a pit of insects.
If you look north you will see
My hidden treasure.
But I forget what it is!

Jonathan Simpson (10)
Pirton Hill Junior School

HIDDEN TREASURES

Pirates were sailing on their best wooden vessel,
Following the map to Treasure Island,

Across the sea,
When the villains arrived,
To their surprise, the X spot was spied.

They all rushed over to dig,
They all opened the box and out jumped a fox,

And what they saw,
No one was sure,
They got to their feet and all ran away.

Luke Davey (11)
Pirton Hill Junior School

THE TIME OF THE FOX

The fox runs through the gates of the farm
Eating and eating the turkeys' feathers.

The fox who is a mother to five,
Trying to bring them food to munch and crunch.

Till they have children of their own
She brings to their world the cracking, crunching bones.

Till one day the mother fox gets caught.
She's eating the turkey, then bang, bang, bang!
Her children never see her again.

Kimberley Dunbar (10)
Pirton Hill Junior School

HIDDEN TREASURES

Far away, deep underground,
nobody knows what people have found.
Over the hills, digging for gold,
nobody know what treasures they hold.
In the sea, it is very deep,
nobody knows what they will seek.
Behind the rocks, it is very dark,
nobody know if there's a glittering spark.
Above the trees is the bright blue sky,
nobody know unless you're a spy!

Keri Murphy (11)
Pirton Hill Junior School

I LIKE

I like seeing flowers bloom in spring,
I like seeing lambs leaping by their mothers,
I like chocolate, sweets and candy,
I like to see birds singing in the treetops,
I like diamond rings,
I like celebrations and going to parties,
I like going on holidays or to the seaside,
I like seeing the waves crashing on the shore,

I like . . .

Nikki-Marie Hetherington (10)
Pirton Hill Junior School

LIONS

Lions are brown,
They pound up and down.
They live in the desert too,
And they want to play with you.

Beware! They might catch you,
And eat you too.
If I give you a clue,
You have to run away too.

Chloe Harle (11)
Pirton Hill Junior School

CHINCHILLA

Chinchillas are fast
They sleep all day
They live in the desert
They're very soft
They eat anything
So please don't eat my socks.
They are kind of grey
They eat food like hay
They jump so high
It looks like they can fly.

Lloyd Cook (11)
Pirton Hill Junior School

CHEETAHS

Cheetahs run like a blaze of fire
Running around like there is no time to waste
Cheetahs live in forests, deserts too
They also like to play with you
Scratches with his awesome claws
And pounds around with his enormous paws
And grinds bones with his bone-crunching jaws
Do not play games or they cheat
Now it's time for them to sleep.

Hannah Bush (10)
Pirton Hill Junior School

THE TIGER

He creeps about hunting for prey
So he will have some food
For the end of the day.
Really fluffy, sometimes cute
Lives in the forest
With its cubs wearing fluffy suits.

Stamps down the grass
Can run very fast
It can jump on you
And squash you too
It's a tiger.

Laura Day (11)
Pirton Hill Junior School

PIRATES ABOARD

In the middle of the ocean
a boat was sailing by,
it was collecting diamonds and crystals,
the diamonds were so shiny and clean.
The crystals sparkled as the diamonds did
but the reason they were sparkling, they were all wet.
The pirates were all drunk and dizzy by all the
turns of the flashing ocean splashing upon the boat.
The pirates called for other pirates to come,
if other boats came near they would shout out
'Hey, bombs away!'

Sarah Thomas (10)
Pirton Hill Junior School

KANGAROO

A hard puncher
A jumbo kicker
A long hopper
A huge jumper
A brown bouncer
A big swinger
A sagging pouch keeper.

Ben Spavins (10)
St Michael's CE Combined School, Stewkley

THE OWL

A night-time hunter
A secret listener
A silent watcher
A swift catcher
A sharp beak
A furry body
A mouse muncher
A wise old bird.

Lucy Collins (11)
St Michael's CE Combined School, Stewkley

THE RUBBER

The rubber, it's cool
It rubs out your writing and
Withdraws your drawing.

Jessica Turner (10)
St Michael's CE Combined School, Stewkley

FROG

A huge hopper
A fly trapper
A springy bopper
A weird croaker
A lily pad hopper
A tadpole maker
A slimy skater
A silent waiter.

Bill Burton (11)
St Michael's CE Combined School, Stewkley

A HAMSTER

A small nibbler
A ball of fluff
A soft feeler
A good healer
A bedding mover
An ultimate hoover
A scared holder
A hand-sized boulder.

Stephanie D'Arcy Collins (11)
St Michael's CE Combined School, Stewkley

SILENCE

Silence has its charm
It does no one any harm
You hear the wind whistle by
The silence will never die
It will always be nearby.

Phillip Swift (11)
St Michael's CE Combined School, Stewkley

SNAKES!

A grass glider,
A desert swinger,
A jungle singer,
A tree hanger,
An eye sharpener,
A fang biter,
A rodent killer,
A mongoose thriller.

Berry Yirrell (11)
St Michael's CE Combined School, Stewkley

THE AARDVARK

A strong sniffer
A termite digger
A fast runner
A quick eater
A long snout
A furry body
A fat belly
And rather smelly.

Robbie Jamie (10)
St Michael's CE Combined School, Stewkley

CARS

Mazdas, Ferraris,
Are all very beautiful
But Porsches are even better.

Ben Chamberlaine (10)
St Michael's CE Combined School, Stewkley

A Dog's Day

A security guard
A noise maker
A bum biter
A bone chewer
A cat chaser
A rescue service
A good runner
A man's best friend.

Tim Whittaker (11)
St Michael's CE Combined School, Stewkley

View Of A Cat

An ankle brusher,
A mouse chaser,
A tail swisher,
A nine lifer,
A fence springer,
A lap sitter,
A wool catcher,
A purr machine.

Lucy Alexandra Kennedy (11)
St Michael's CE Combined School, Stewkley

The Owl

The owl is nimble, silent,
Waiting for its prey to come,
Down as light as air,
Targeting its prey, crush, squeak.
At last he now has meat.

Paul Terry (11)
St Michael's CE Combined School, Stewkley

A Toad

A fly trapper
A show stopper
A fat squelcher
A low belcher
A lily flopper
A duckweed shaker
A slimy skater
A terrible waiter.

Jack Howe (10)
St Michael's CE Combined School, Stewkley

Failing Friend

Two-faced friend she is
  Lying, cheating, failing friend
    Tries to make it up
      But she can't keep promises
        A forever failing friend.

Rebecca Jane Carr (11)
St Michael's CE Combined School, Stewkley

Monkey

Monkey, monkey, you are so funky,
When you're swinging all day and night,
You look so funny, you look like your mummy,
Oh monkey, you are so funky.

David Winsor (10)
St Michael's CE Combined School, Stewkley

THE SUN AND THE MOON

The moon is our moon,
It sails round us like pirates in a lagoon,
It has a place in the sky,
Like a giant's apple pie.

The sun provides light,
It floats high above us, like a big yellow kite,
But gradually we go round the sun,
You may not realise it, but it might be fun.

The moon comes out at night,
At a tremendous height,
It sails above us,
Making a big fuss.

Maybe the sun is jealous of the moon,
Because it comes out at night,
Or maybe they both have a part to play,
The sun provides light and a moon at night!

One day someone was travelling at night,
And the moon his eye like a big apple pie
He saw it floating there up in the sky
And would always be high.

Mikey Digby (11)
St Michael's CE Combined School, Stewkley

THE MAGIC SPIDER

Spinning all day long
With its magic fine silk thread
Work for a spider.

Charlotte Cooper (11)
St Michael's CE Combined School, Stewkley

THE PIED PIPER OF HAMELIN

In Hamelin, Germany,
There were as many rats as there could be!
'Get rid of these rats!' the townspeople cried,
'Or we'll get rid of you as if you've died!'
At this, the Mayor lost his cool,
And started panicking, what a fool!
In his chamber eating soup,
He moaned, 'We'll need a troop
Of people to get rid of the rats,
I just hope that they don't wear hats!'
Just then, there was a knock at the door,
The poor Mayor thought it was a rat on the floor!
Then, striding in came a man,
Who bellowed 'The rats, I can ban!
All it will take is a thousand guilders,
And I will charm them with my magic wonders!'
'Then,' said the Mayor, 'come in, come in,
would you like a biscuit from the tin?
Your offer is absolutely marvellous,
Go ahead, impress us.'
The piper, in his piped suit,
Stepped out on the street and played a toot,
After that he played a tune,
And all the rats followed the wonderful boom,
The piper, he walked into the lake,
That's where the rats met their fate.
He then walked back to collect his pay,
To find it had been used to save the day,
Only fifty guilders were left from the building
So he went off with it, weeping.

Daniel Dawson (11)
St Michael's CE Combined School, Stewkley

A Horse

The small dished face stretches out for a mint,
The velvet lips brush your hand as she accepts a treat,
Then she thrusts her soft, warm muzzle into your pocket for more,
Her ears prick, her curious eyes watching your every move
                    as you reach into your pocket for another.
And then she's off with her flowing mane and coat sparkling
                                        in the evening dusk.
The dainty hooves and slender legs make the perfect gaits.
And with her tail held high, she gallops away.

A dream horse

Meg Ratcliffe (11)
St Michael's CE Combined School, Stewkley

An Old Garden Hose

Swaying all around
Like a poisonous cobra
An old garden hose.

Matthew Alexander (10)
St Michael's CE Combined School, Stewkley

Wolf

It's eating the meat with its paws
In the wood, growling, vicious,
White and black and it's in the dark.

It hears an owl
It runs away into the woods.

Daniel Mangan (11)
Weatherfield School

MONKEY

I want a monkey
Any kind of monkey
A funny monkey
A stupid monkey
A fat monkey
A cute monkey

I want a monkey
Any kind of monkey
A quiet monkey
A noisy monkey
A black monkey
A brown monkey

I want a monkey
Any kind of monkey.

Simon Hassan (11)
Weatherfield School

ELEPHANT

I wish I had an elephant
That had a long trunk.
I'd feed it lemons and grass.

I wish I had an elephant
I'd play with him all day
We would play football together.

I wish I had an elephant
I'd take him for a walk.
But I wish there were more elephants like him.

Alexander Sheehan (11)
Weatherfield School

PARROT

I want a parrot.
Any kind of parrot.
A parrot of different colours.
Colours like purple, red, green,
Blue, yellow and orange.
It will sing me to sleep
And it will wake me up.

Emma Coggins (11)
Weatherfield School

TIGER

A tiger runs fast.
He can see things from afar.
His teeth are really sharp.
He's got a stripy coat.
It keeps him really warm.
It camouflages the tiger in the dark.
He's a good hunter.
They are becoming extinct.
I think tigers are smart.

Joshua Shadbolt (11)
Weatherfield School

PENGUINS

Penguins are black, white and yellow
They waddle on the ice.

Penguins make me laugh
The way they walk together

I've seen some at the zoo
Jumping over the bridge

I would really like to own one
So it could teach me how to dive.

Kieran Towers (10)
Weatherfield School

MY DOGS

My dogs, Charlie and Tyson, like football.
They play it anywhere they like.

They are brown and black
They jump over a log saying *'Woof.'*

They are *vicious* and *mad* dogs

I love my dogs.

Wayne Dawes (11)
Weatherfield School

GUINEA PIGS

Where do guinea pigs hide and sleep at night?
They feed and they are cuddly
They are very furry.
I take them out of the cage.
They are sweet and tiny
They are babies and I love them very much.
I feed them and they are nice pets.

Coleen Welland (11)
Weatherfield School

MY RABBIT

My rabbit is friendly,
She is furry
And cuddly.
A rabbit has babies.
They are in a nest.
The mother keeps them warm.
They get bigger,
Then start all over again.

Laura Strange (10)
Weatherfield School

MY FISHES

Fishes like me very much.
Fishes like their food.
Fishes like to do tricks.
Fishes like to swim.
I love my fishes very much.
I love them.

Jamie Edwards (10)
Weatherfield School

DOG

My favourite dog is an Alsation.
My garden is big enough.
My parents always say
'No, it's too big.'
But I will never give up.
I want an Alsation.

Michael Winchester (10)
Weatherfield School

GUINEA PIGS

I want a guinea pig
So I can stroke it all the time.
I would like to play with it.
Guinea pigs are friendly.
Guinea pigs are cuddly and furry.
Guinea pigs play and fight together.
Guinea pigs like to be held.
I want a guinea pig.

Jenny Mroz (10)
Weatherfield School

MY DOGS

My dogs are called Meg and Penny
Meg's black and white and Penny's brown
Penny goes in my room at night
Meg wakes me up and she looks out of my window
Meg and Penny have a fight
I think Meg and Penny are good dogs.

Thomas Tillier (10)
Weatherfield School

MY RABBIT

My rabbit is cool
But he's not small.
When I get a bit of straw he bites it.
My rabbit is fun.
My rabbit is black.
I love my rabbit.

Daniel Phillips (11)
Weatherfield School

MY LION

My lion is white and fluffy.
My lion does tricks.
My lion likes meat.
My lion is friendly.
My lion helps me.
My lion has a smart brain like me.
My lion tells me jokes.
When I'm ill it looks after me.
I'll love my lion for ever and ever.

Leo Morawski (11)
Weatherfield School

DOLPHINS

Dolphins are friendly
Dolphins can jump
Dolphins can swim fast in the sea
Dolphins can talk
Dolphins eat fish
Dolphins are squeaky and loud
Dolphins play with a ball
Dolphins can splash me
I want to swim with the dolphins.

Kerrie West (10)
Weatherfield School

HORSES

I love horses
Horses can be black and white
Horses have babies called foals
Foals grow and grow into a horse
Then they give birth to a foal

I would love to have a horse
I could ride it in lots of fields
Horses live in stables
They eat grass
Some horses are in danger
I love horses.

Elizabeth Andrews (11)
Weatherfield School

SOLO, MY CAT

I want a cat who sleeps on the mat.
I want a cat who is very fat.
I want a cat who smells like a rat.
I want a cat who likes a pat.
I want a cat who eats all the fat.
I want a cat who runs like a rat.
But I like him any way.

Richard Bygrave (10)
Weatherfield School

MY HAMSTER

My hamster is called Gizmo.
He wakes me up at night.
He runs around his wheel.
And gives me a fright.
I take him out of his cage
And hold him in my hand.
He wiggles and jiggles
And bites me on the hand.

Samuel Brunt (10)
Weatherfield School

FROG

I want a frog
Any kind of frog

A jumpy frog
A flying frog

I want a frog
Any kind of frog

A slimy frog
A sandy frog

I want a frog
Any kind of frog

A loud frog
A quiet frog

I want a frog
Any kind of frog

A shy frog
A bold frog

I want a frog
Any kind of frog

A green frog
A black frog

I want a frog!

Lewis Cox (11)
Weatherfield School

CROCODILES

Crocodiles are big and they have sharp teeth.
They live on the bank of the river.
What they see, they eat.
Crocodiles live in the zoo and in hot countries.
Crocodiles live in the wet parts.
The crocodiles go in pairs.
They go in lakes and rivers.
The crocodiles eat meat.
Crocodiles are very fierce.
Crocodiles live in Australia.
Crocodiles eat humans.
Crocodiles hide under the water.
Crocodiles go for their enemies.
I love crocodiles.

Alec Hill (10)
Weatherfield School